# BLUE ARMY QUIZ BOOK

## LEICESTER CITY

### NIGEL FREESTONE

DB
PUBLISHING

First published in Great Britain in 2012 by The Derby Books Publishing Company Limited, 3 The Parker
Centre, Derby, DE21 4SZ.

ISBN 978-1-78091-048-2

Printed and bound by Gomer Press, Llandysul, Ceredigion.

# BLUE ARMY QUIZ BOOK

## LEICESTER CITY

# Contents

# Leicester Fosse FC

From its humble beginnings as Leicester Fosse, founded at the end of the 19th century inside a wooden hut near the Roman Fosse Way, Leicester City has become one of the dozen or so best supported football clubs in Great Britain. The history of Leicester City is a remarkable story which for season after season has catapulted its blue army of fans on an emotional roller coaster of highs and lows. Never a dull moment, the Foxes past, like its present, is crammed full of remarkable victories, crushing defeats, League Championships, Cup wins, relegation battles, promotion drives, controversy, as well as a plentiful supply of villains and heroes.

At the beginning of 2003 after New Fox PLC acquired Leicester City a proposal was made to change the name of the club back to Leicester Fosse, which was rejected by the fans.

How much do you know about the original Leicester Fosse?

# In the Beginning...

1.    In what year was Leicester Fosse Football Club founded?
a)    1883
b)    1884
c)    1887

2.    Were the following Midland clubs formed before or after Leicester Fosse. In other words, are they Younger or Older?
a)    Nottingham Forest. Younger or Older?
b)    Coventry City. Younger or Older?
c)    Derby County. Younger or Older?
d)    Birmingham City. Younger or Older?
e)    Lincoln City. Younger or Older?
f)    Peterborough United. Younger or Older?
g)    Northampton Town. Younger or Older?

3.    The old boys of which school founded Leicester Fosse?

4.    Frank Gardner is often referred to as the 'founder father of the Fosse'. How old was he when he was elected secretary and treasurer at the formative meeting of the club?
a)    17
b)    39
c)    63

5.    What does the word 'Fosse' mean?
a)    road
b)    ditch
c)    hedge

6.    Within a few months of the formation of Leicester Fosse, and after numerous practice sessions, a fixture list was drawn up of at least a dozen games. Leicester Fosse played their inaugural fixture, a home game against Syston Fosse. How much do you know about this momentous event?

a) Where was the game played?
   i) Belgrave Road Sports Ground
   ii) Victoria Park
   iii) private field off Fosse Road
b) What colour shirts did the Fosse wear?
   i) black and blue stripes
   ii) chocolate and cream quarters
   iii) black with a diagonal blue sash
c) According to a local newspaper, what formation did the Fosse play?
   i) 1–3–6
   ii) 2–4–4
   iii) 2–3–5
d) What was the final score?
   i) Leicester Fosse 5–0 Syston Fosse
   ii) Leicester Fosse 0–5 Syston Fosse
   iii) Leicester Fosse 12–0 Syston Fosse
e) Which of the following football features were present?
   i) crossbar
   ii) goal nets
   iii) corner flags
   iv) managers dugout
   v) white football

7. Football has changed considerably since Leicester Fosse was founded. Not just the finances, media coverage, stadia and the public profile of players, but also the rules. Determine whether the following were allowed in Fosse's first game. In other words can you sort out the Fair from the Foul?

a) The goalkeeper is about to save a shot when he's suddenly charged over by an opponent, resulting in the ball flying into the goal. Fair or Foul?
b) A player takes a throw-in with one hand. Fair or Foul?
c) The goalkeeper catches the ball outside the penalty area and charges down the pitch bouncing the ball and unleashes a shot at the opposition goal from near the halfway line. Fair or Foul?
d) After a player puts the ball behind his own goal, a free kick is awarded. Fair or Foul?

e)     Having been awarded a penalty, instead of kicking the ball the player dribbles the ball past the goalkeeper to score. Fair or Foul?

f)     At a free kick the opponent players stand just 6 yards away from the ball. Fair of Foul?

g)     The defender in a goal-line clearance heads the ball over the crossbar. Fair or Foul?

8.     At the end of their first season, having played 15 games (W8, D4, L3), the Fosse managed to make how much profit?

a)     1d

b)     10d

c)     1s 10d

9.     What was Leicester Fosse's nickname?

10.     Why was the match between Coalville and the Fosse in 1886–87 abandoned?

a)     the local constabulary arrested two of the Coalville players for blasphemy

b)     a lightning strike hit a tree which fell onto the pitch narrowly missing the Fosse goalkeeper

c)     the Coalville side walked off the pitch refusing to accept an umpire decision

11.     The Bonfire day match against Burton Swifts in 1887 marked a red letter day in the relatively short history of Leicester Fosse. Why?

a)     the attendance at a Fosse home game exceeded 1,000 for the first time

b)     spectators were charged an entrance fee to watch the Fosse play for the first time

c)     the Fosse played in royal blue shirts for the first time

12.     In 1887 Leicester Fosse moved from Victoria Park to their first enclosed ground. Where was it?

a)     Belgrave Road Sports Ground

b)     Melton Road Sports Ground

c)     Walnut Street

13. The Fosse had to vacate their new home in 1888 after just one season. Why?
a) they were evicted having failed to pay the rent for the ground (£2 3s) on time
b) they were outbid for the use of the facilities by the Leicester Tigers
c) the ground was subject to a compulsory purchase order by the Council and redeveloped as a shoe factory

14. Leicester Fosse's first-ever Cup match, in October 1887, against St Saviours at Belgrave Road in the Leicestershire Association Cup ended in controversy. Why?
a) Fosse's 4–2 win was declared void after St Saviours protested over the poor light in which the game ended
b) Fosse had played all of the second half of the game with 13 players, which was not noticed until the end of the game
c) the umpire blew the final whistle 11 minutes early and was accused by St Saviours of favouring the Fosse, for whom his brother was a player

15. The Fosse eventually overcame St Saviours and were knocked out in round two by which north Leicestershire club, who subsequently went on to become the first holders of the trophy?
a) Shepshed Albion
b) Coalville Town
c) Loughborough Corithinians

16. What was the first trophy won by Leicester Fosse?
a) Leicestershire Senior Cup
b) Leicestershire Hospitals Cup
c) Leicester Association Challenge Cup

17. What was the name given to Leicester Fosse's reserve team founded in 1886?

18. Leicester Fosse's first professional player, Harry Webb was signed in 1888. What was his starting salary?

a)      2s 6d a week
b)      12s 6d a week
c)      6d a match

19.     In mid-December 1890, despite a thick fog shrouding the ground, a record crowd of 2,500 (gate receipts of £23) attended Mill Lane to watch the Fosse draw 1–1 against arch-rivals Loughborough Town. Ten minutes or so after the final whistle, with the players back in the changing room, it was noticed that the Fosse goalie, Charlie Walker was missing. Where was he found?

a)      still out on the pitch standing by an upright unaware that the game had ended
b)      unconscious, so thick was the fog that he walked into one of the avenue of trees marking the boundary of the ground, knocking himself out, as he tried to find his way to the changing room
c)      in Loughborough Town's changing room. He signed for them at the end of the match without the knowledge of his manager

20.     The first 'football special' train took some 1,500 Fosse fans to which town in February 1891?

# Midland League Fosse

21. Seven years after their formation Leicester Fosse gained entry to the 12-team Midland League, which had been formed in 1889, just one step away from the Football League.

a) What colour shirt and shorts did the Fosse wear in their opening Midland League season?
   i) blue shirts and white breeches
   ii) blue and white striped shirts and blue breeches
   iii) white shirts and blue breeches

b) Where did the Fosse play their first Midland League home games before moving to Walnut Street?
   i) Victoria Park Rugby FC Ground
   ii) Mill Lane Sports Stadium
   iii) Aylestone Road County Cricket Ground

c) Who were their first opponents in the Midand League?
   i) Derby Railwaymen
   ii) Derby Junction
   iii) Derby County

d) At what time did the Fosse's opening Midland League game kick-off?
   i) 11.40am
   ii) 3.15pm
   iii) 4.50pm

e) The Fosse's first Midland League game was refereed by William Clark, who later became?
   i) England coach
   ii) Fosse's manager
   iii) Deputy Prime Minister

f) What was the final score the Fosse's opening fixture in the Midland League?

g) How many points were the Fosse awarded for winning the game?
   i) 2 points
   ii) 3 points
   iii) 4 points

22. The Fosse won their opening two Midland League fixtures, both at home. Their first away League game was at Burton Wanderers. What was the final score?
a) Burton Wanderers 6–0 Leicester Fosse
b) Burton Wanderers 6–6 Leicester Fosse
c) Burton Wanderers 0–6 Leicester Fosse

23. Leicester Fosse moved to Walnut Street ground, later renamed Filbert Street, in 1891. Their first opponents at their new ground were Loughborough Town, a game which they lost 2–1. It was not until January 1892 that the club won their first Midland League game at Walnut Street by demolishing which South Yorkshire club, the eventual Midland League Champions, 4–1?

24. Leicester Fosse finished their first Midland League season in what position?
a) 3rd
b) 7th
c) 11th

25. The Fosse played all of the following clubs in the Midland League apart from ONE. Can you identify the impostor?
a) Long Eaton Rangers
b) Notts Olympic
c) Mansfield Greenhalgh
d) Kettering
e) Grantham Rovers
f) Wednesbury Old Athletic

26. The Fosse played three seasons in the Midland League, between 1891 and 1894. What was their highest end-of-season League position?
a) 1st (Champions)
b) 2nd (runners-up)
c) 3rd

27. The Fosse's worst defeat in the Midland League was an 11–0 thumping away at which club?

a)    Newark
b)    Rotherham Town
c)    Chesterfield

28.   Leicester Fosse slaughtered Newark at home in October 1892,
      to record the club's best win in the Midland League. What was
      the final score?
a)    Leicester Fosse 7–1 Newark
b)    Leicester Fosse 9–2 Newark
c)    Leicester Fosse 11–1 Newark

29.   Just two weeks before the start of the 1892–93 Midland League
      season, the Fosse were invited to replace New Brighton Tower
      upon their belated resignation from Football League Division
      Two. Fosse's committee, who felt they were bound by honour to
      the Midland League, turned down the invitation. True or False?

30.   What was the highest transfer fee Leicester Fosse received for a
      player while playing in the Midland League?
a)    £2 10s
b)    £25
c)    £250

# FA Cup Fosse

31. The FA Challenge Cup, the oldest football competition in the world, 'for which all clubs belonging to the Football Association should be invited to join' began in 1871 more than a dozen years before Leicester Fosse were even formed. Based on the inter-house knock-out competition at Harrow School, just 15 clubs entered the first competition, with the Wanderers beating the Royal Engineers 1–0 at the Oval in the Final. The magic of the FA Cup, which has to-date always ended in tears has brought tremendous excitement and disappointment to Leicester ever since the club played it's first-ever FA Cup tie, a first round qualifier, on 4 October 1890.

a) Who were their opponents?
   i) Burton Town
   ii) Burton Albion
   iii) Burton Wanderers

b) Where was the Cup tie played?
   i) Mill Lane, Leicester
   ii) Victoria Park, Leicester
   iii) Victoria Park, Burton

c) What colour shirts did the Fosse wear?
   i) black
   ii) blue
   iii) white

d) The Fosse lost the game. What was the final score?
   i) 0–2
   ii) 0–4
   iii) 0–8

e) What were the gate receipts for the Cup tie?
   i) £5
   ii) £15
   iii) £22

32. Small Heath mauled the Fosse 2–6 in the FA Qualifying competition in the 1891–92 season. By what name are Small Heath now known?

33. As the 1890–91 season came to an end, a record crowd of 3,500 spectators attended Mill Lane to watch the Fosse play against the beaten FA Cup finalists and their first opponents from the newly formed Football League. Which club did Fosse draw 2–2 with that day?

34. Leicester Fosse beat Loughborough Town 1–0 away from home in December 1893 to reach the FA Cup first round proper. The game was a fraught affair involving a 34 minute delay. What was the cause of the delay?
a) fighting between Loughborough Town and Leicester Fosse fans
b) the primitive floodlight system failed
c) the Loughborough Town captain had his broken leg set by a doctor while still on the pitch

35. In the round two, Division One Derby County beat the Fosse 3–0 after drawing 0–0 at Leicester. The Rams skipper appeared in court and was fined £5 for what offence, which took place during the game?
a) assaulting the referee
b) assaulting Fosse's manager
c) assaulting a spectator

36. Leicester Fosse slaughtered Notts Olympic in the first qualifying round of the FA Cup in October 1894. How many goals did the Fosse score in the Cup tie?
a) 11
b) 12
c) 13

37. Kettering Town knocked the Fosse out of the FA Cup competition for three consecutive years during the 1890s. True or False?

38. In which season were the Fosse given automatic entry to the first round proper of the FA Cup competition?

39. Which Southern League outfit caused an upset by dumping the Fosse out of the FA Cup in 1897?
a) Portsmouth
b) Southampton
c) Plymouth

40. Name the Leicestershire club which reached the second round of the FA Cup in 2004, that were knocked out of the competition 109 years earlier by Leicester Fosse?

41. Name the two Northamptonshire clubs the Fosse played during the 1902–03 FA Cup campaign?
a) Irthlingborough and Wellingborough
b) Rushden and Kettering
c) Kettering and Northampton Town

42. Why was the replayed FA Cup tie between the Fosse and Burton United at Leicester in 1903 abandoned during extra-time, with the score at 2–2?
a) torrential downpour flooded the pitch
b) bad light
c) one of the goal posts was struck by lightning

43. Leicester Fosse slaughtered which other Leicestershire club 10–0 in an FA Cup tie in 1903?

44. What was unusual about Mr J. Talks who refereed the FA Cup tie in 1912 between the Fosse and Chelsea played at Croydon Common?
a) he had two artificial legs
b) he was just 4ft 9in tall
c) he was partially sighted

45. What was significant about the Fosse's exit from the FA Cup in December 1914 by Swansea Town?

a)   it was the first and only time that Leicester City/Fosse had been knocked out of the FA Cup by a Welsh club

b)   it was Leicester's last defeat by non-League opposition until Harlow Town in 1980

c)   it was the only match in which Leicester City/Fosse were awarded four penalties and missed them all

# Football League Fosse

The Football League began in 1888, comprising just one division of 12 clubs. A Division Two was inaugurated some four years later, after the Division One had expanded to 16 teams. The Fosse were elected to Division Two of the Football League in 1894 and played a 30 game opening campaign.

46.      The Fosse's first-ever Football League game was away from home in August 1894.

a)      Who were Fosse's opponents on that historical day?
- i)  Grimsby Town
- ii)  Darwen
- iii) Burslem Port Vale

b)      Who is credited with scoring Leicester's first Football League goal?

c)      William McArthur scored Leicester's second goal of the game. According to a newspaper report what was Whitehouse, the opponent's goalkeeper, doing at the time?
- i)  pulling up his socks
- ii)  fighting with a spectator
- iii) smoking a cigar

d)      The game was a particularly memorable one for Fosse player, Horace Bailey. Why?
- i)  he broke his leg on his debut and retired from professional football without having actually kicked the ball
- ii)  he became the first Fosse player to score an own-goal in the Football League
- iii) he was sacked by the Fosse for not trying

e)      What was the final score?
- i)  4–3
- ii)  4–5
- iii) 4–2

f)      What was the attendance?
- i)  500
- ii)  1,500
- iii) 5,000

47. Who managed Fosse's crucial first campaign in the Football League?

48. Who were the Fosse's opponents in the first Football League game staged at Filbert Street?
a) Derby County
b) Nottingham Forest
c) Rotherham Town

49. In the first Football League game staged at Filbert Street, which the Fosse won 4–2, who claimed the club's first Football League hat-trick?

50. What was the cheapest admission price to watch the Fosse play at home in their first season in the Football League?
a) 3d
b) 6d
c) 9d

51. How many goals did Leicester Fosse score in the second half of the Division Two game against Walsall Town Swifts in January 1895?

52. Leicester Fosse drew 3–3 away against Woolwich Arsenal in March 1895. Where was the game played?
a) Highbury
b) Hyde Park
c) Essex County Cricket Ground

53. Why was the admission price at Filbert Street reduced by 2d during the course of the club's first Football League season?
a) the club were ordered by the Football League to reduce their admission prices to make them in-line with other clubs
b) financial hardship experienced by many supporters in a lock-out in the local boot and shoe industry
c) the club wished to thank its loyal fans who had raised money to build a 1,500 capacity main stand

54. What was the average home attendance for the Fosse in their first Football League season?
a) 6,000
b) 9,000
c) 12,000

55. David Skea scored 23 League goals for the Fosse in their first season in the Football League. How many other players managed to score 20 or more League goals for the Fosse in a season?

56. In what position did the Fosse finish in Division Two at the end of their first Football League campaign?
a) 2nd (runners-up)
b) 4th
c) 8th

57. The Fosse played several away games during their first couple of seasons in the Football League at cricket grounds. Can you identify the football clubs that were based at the following cricket grounds?
a) Trent Bridge
b) Essex County Cricket Club
c) Bramall Lane

58. What did Willie 'Tout' Miller miss, the first one that Fosse had ever been awarded in a Football League game, against Newcastle United on 20 October 1894?

59. Why was the Division Two Football League game between Darwen and Leicester Fosse abandoned after just two minutes on 30 December 1894?
a) the Darwen goalkeeper William Freestone was seriously injured by a bolt of lightning
b) the goal posts were blown by a gale
c) the umpire collapsed and died

60. Name the Leicestershire team the Fosse regularly played against in Football League matches at the end of the 19th century?

61. Which two Cup competitions did the Fosse win during the 1896–97 season?
a) Burford Charity Cup and Rushden Charity Cup
b) Diamonds Cup and Rushden Hospital Cup
c) Irthlingborough Charity Cup and Rushden Senior Cup

62. When did Leicester Fosse become a Limited Company?
a) 1896
b) 1897
c) 1898

63. Willie Freebairn became the first Leicester Fosse player to be sent off in a Football League match at Lincoln in April 1897. What was his offence?
a) spitting
b) haranguing a linesman
c) ungentlemanly attire

64. Jimmy Thraves made his 148th and final consecutive appearances in goal for Leicester Fosse against Newton Heath in 1897. By what name are Newton Heath now known?

65. Which club's first-ever Football League game was against Fosse on the opening day of the 1897–98 season?
a) Luton Town
b) Lincoln Town
c) Liverpool

66. The Fosse lost in the Final of the Burford Cup in 1898. The Final was the last game which club played on their old Town Ground, prior to moving to their current home, the City Ground?
a) Lincoln City
b) Notts County
c) Nottingham Forest

67. The Football League match between the Fosse and Wednesday in November 1899 attracted a record Filbert Street attendance of?
a) 12,000
b) 15,000
c) 18,000

68. In which year did the Fosse players wear shorts instead of breeches?
a) 1898
b) 1899
c) 1900

69. Why was Luton Town's ground closed as a result of the Fosse slaughtering them 6–1 in January 1899?
a) crowd disturbances and attempts by the home fans to assault the referee
b) part of the main Stand at Kingswell ground collapsed as 'Hatters' fans rushed to the exits after the Fosse scored their sixth goal
c) the pitch was found to be 1ft 6in too small to stage Football League games

70. What was unusual about the Fosse's 1–2 home defeat to New Brighton Tower in the penultimate game of the 1899–1900 season?
a) it was Fosse's 12th consecutive home defeat, a club record
b) it was the only game during the 1899–1900 season in which they failed to score more two or more goals
c) it was Fosse's first home defeat in 39 Football League games

71. Fosse played a friendly game against which international FA side in October 1899, just a few weeks before war broke out between them and Great Britain?
a) France
b) South Africa
c) Holland

72. In which year did the Fosse sit on top of Division Two of the Football League for the first-time in the club's history?

73.    The maximum wage for professional footballers at Football League level came into force in 1901. What was the maximum weekly wage?

74.    Why was there an unexpected mid-season break in late-January and early February 1901?

75.    The Fosse started the 1901–02 season in a new strip. What colour shirts did they wear?
a)    two-tone combination of dark blue with light blue collars and sleeves
b)    blue and white quarters with light blue collars and sleeves
c)    dark blue and light blue thin stripes with dark blue collars and white cuffs

76.    What was the name given to the Fosse's own matchday programme?
a)    The *Fosse Times*
b)    The *Fosse Chronicle*
c)    The *Fosse Mercury*

77.    A 3–1 Leicester Fosse away win at Burnley in January 1903 would have been even more comprehensive had a shot by Tom Simpson not?
a)    hit a stray dog on the goal-line
b)    hit the referee who was standing in front of an open goal
c)    been saved by a spectator who had ran onto the pitch

78.    Why did the Fosse face re-election to the Football League at the end of the 1903–04 season?
a)    as a part of the punishment handed out by the Football League after finding the club guilty of three counts of financial irregularities
b)    due to a boycott of away games by leading players, the club failed to complete all of the fixtures
c)    because they finished bottom of Division Two

79.   Football League rules stated prior to 1904 that Leicester Fosse
      players had to wear?
a)    shorts that were below the knees
b)    leather boots with metal studs
c)    shirts with cuffs and collars in a contrasting colour

80.   How many players made their debut for the Fosse in the opening
      game of the 1904–05 season, away at Blackpool?
a)    7
b)    9
c)    10

81.   The Fosse splashed out how much money, at the time a club
      record fee, to acquire the services of the former England centre-
      half Billy Banister in 1904?
a)    £39
b)    £395
c)    £3,950

82.   Which club, newly elected to Division Two, recorded their first
      win in the Football League against the Fosse in 1905?
a)    Leeds United
b)    Leeds Rovers
c)    Leeds City

83.   Until 1908 what colour jersey did Leicester Fosse's goalkeeper wear?
a)    green
b)    black
c)    the same colour as the outfield players

84.   Why were the streets surrounding Leicester's London Road
      Midland Railway Station overflowing with a celebrating crowd
      as the Fosse players returned from Football League game at
      Stoke City in April 1908?

85.   A crowd of about 15,000 spectators on 1 September 1908
      watched the Fosse play their first game in Division One. Who
      were their opponents?

a)    Sheffield Wednesday
b)    Sheffield United
c)    Sheffield Olympics

86.    The third game from the end of the Fosse's opening campaign in the top flight in English football, against Nottingham Forest, put the club into the record books for all the wrong reasons. Why?

87.    Did Leicester Fosse ever score a goal direct from a corner kick?

88.    In what League position did the Fosse finish their first campaign in the top-flight of English football?
a)    13th
b)    17th
c)    20th

89.    In October 1908 Leicester Fosse met Blackburn Rovers at Peel Croft, Burton in an 'experimental' friendly which Rovers won 3–1. What was 'experimental' about the game?
a)    the game was played at night under the lights of electric arc lamps suspended around and over the ground
b)    the players wore numbered shirts, with Rovers players numbered 1 to 11 and the Fosse numbered 12 to 22
c)    the game was officiated by two referees and two linesmen

90.    The Fosse paid a club record fee of £625 to Bradford City in January 1909 to secure the services of striker Wallace Smith. Like so many that would follow, he was a flop never shining in a Fosse shirt let alone scoring a goal. Smith was transferred to Hull City after just six appearances for £500. True or False?

91.    Who scored an amazing 32 League goals for Leicester Fosse in the 1909–10 season, a club record that remained until the days of Arthur Chandler?

92.    The Fosse persuaded 33-year-old former Wolverhampton Wanderers and West Bromwich Albion centre-half, Ted

Pheasant, to sign in July 1910. However, he never played a competitive game for the club. Why?

a) he died of peritonitis in Leicester Infirmary within two weeks of his transfer

b) he was transferred to Birmingham City two days after signing for the Fosse after a fight with the manager

c) he became a MP after winning the Birmingham Ladywood by-election for the Liberal Party and quit football

93. Why was Billy Mills, a young Fosse forward suspended by the FA for two months in 1911?

a) for playing football on a Sunday

b) for being homosexual

c) for adultery

94. In 1912 the Fosse played a series of friendly matches to raise money for which disaster fund?

95. In 1913, the Fosse embarked on their first-ever foreign tour, an all-expenses paid trip to which country?

a) Sweden

b) Switzerland

c) Spain

96. Why was Christmas Day 1913, a memorable one for Fosse player Tom Waterall?

a) he scored a hat-trick on his Fosse debut just 24 hours after scoring four times in his final game for Everton

b) he played for Fosse reserves in the morning and the first team in the afternoon

c) he broke his leg after tripping while running onto the Filbert Street pitch in a Football League game against Nottingham Forest and never played again for the club

97. Why were the Fosse known nationally as the '£105 team' during the 1913–14 season?

98. Why did Leicester Fosse change their strip from the now traditional blue shirts to blue and white stripes throughout World War One?
a) blue dye was hard to obtain
b) stripes were thought to be more patriotic
c) the German international side used to play in royal blue shirts

99. How many players did the Fosse use during the 36 fixtures of the 1916–17 campaign?
a) 12
b) 37
c) 72

100. Why did the Fosse play in an all magenta kit in their League game away at Grimsby in January 1917?
a) they had to borrow a strip from a local club after losing their kit on the journey to Blundell Park
b) they had just purchased a new blue strip, which dramatically changed colour upon washing
c) magenta was the most abundant and cheapest dye available during World War One and as a consequence many clubs when they changed their strip chose magenta

101. What bizarre incident occurred to Leicester Fosse's goalie, Herbert Brown in an away match at Bradford City in October 1917?
a) he saved four penalties in the game
b) as he was preparing to take a goal kick a dog ran from the crowd behind him and he unwittingly landed a kick on the dog instead of the ball
c) he was knocked unconscious after the wooden crossbar fell onto his head after a shot from a hefty 16 stone Bradford striker dislodged it from the goal posts

102. On 22 December 1917 Fosse beat Bradford Park Avenue 1–0 away from home in a Football League Midlands game. Why did the game, which was not abandoned, last just 52 minutes?
a) the game was played under wartime regulations of 50 minutes duration, with no half-time

b)      the train carrying Fosse players arrived so late that the game had to end when darkness fell

c)      Fosse had arranged to play Bradford City the same day in another 50 minute game

103.     Leicester Fosse played their last game on 26 April 1919 against Birmingham City. Did the Fosse win, lose or draw the game?

104.     Who was the only player to score more than 50 goals for Leicester Fosse?

105.     How many seasons did the Fosse spend in the topflight of English football?

106.     How many games did the Fosse win in Division One?
a)      1
b)      5
c)      8

107.     What was the highest position the Fosse finished a Football League campaign?
a)      5th Division One
b)      20th Division One
c)      22nd Division One

108.     What was the highest number of goals the Fosse scored in a Football League season?
a)      79
b)      89
c)      99

109.     What was the highest transfer fee the Fosse ever received for a player?
a)      £250
b)      £500
c)      £1,000

110. How many times were the Fosse forced to seek re-election to the Football League?

111. The Fosse never lost against arch-rivals Loughborough Town in the Football League. True or False?

112. When Leicester Fosse was officially wound-up at the end of the 1918–19 season, how much was the club in debt?
a)  £300
b)  £3,000
c)  £30,000

On 14 June 1919, four days after the visit of King George V and Queen Mary, the Home Secretary wrote to the Mayor, restoring Leicester's status as a city, after an interval of some 700 years. The Limited Company which purchased Leicester Fosse's assets, which included the players transfers for £4,000, capitalised on this event by registering the new Company under the name The Leicester City Football Club Company Limited...the rest as they say is history.

# Nicknames

113.   Leicester have been known as the Fossils, Ancients. Filberts and Foxes. Nicknames can provide fascinating insight into the history of a football club. Are the following origins of club nicknames True or False?

a)   Notts County's nickname 'The Magpies' was derived from their black and white kit. True or False?

b)   Derby County was founded by a group of shepherds in the Dales, hence the nickname 'The Rams'. True or False?

c)   Nottingham Forest became known as 'Forest' because their first ground was located on the edge of Sherwood Forest. True or False?

d)   Peterborough United's nickname 'The Posh' came from the fact that the club was founded in the 1930s by former students of an elite public school. True or False?

e)   Aston Villa are known as 'The Villians' after the Villa Cross church in Aston. True or False?

f)   The 'Silkmen', Macclesfield Town's nickname is derived from the name of their first ground – Silkmoor. True or False?

g)   Chesterfield are known as the 'Spirites' because of the famous twisted spire on the church in town. True or False?

114.   The following nicknames are of clubs City played in their first season in the top flight of English Football in 1908–09. How many clubs can you correctly name?

a)   The Owls

b)   The Mariners

c)   The Shakers

d)   The Blades

e)   The Bantams

f)   The Lilywhites

g)   The Robins

h)   The Toffeemen

115. Footballers are not often renowned for their eloquence, referring to teammates by nicknames which often end with a 'y', such as 'Giggsy', 'Bally'. The following former Leicester players' nicknames are marginally more imaginative. How many players can you identify?

a) Sid
b) The Tank
c) Channy
d) Sniffer
e) Bruno
f) The Wasp
g) Geordie
h) The Doug

# A Year You Remember?

In what year did the following groups of events occur?

116.    Mark Draper became City's first £1 million signing; reserve team games were designated as Family Night Football; Leicester City played their first game in the FA Premier League.
a)    1990
b)    1992
c)    1994

117.    City slaughtered Portsmouth 10–0 at Filbert Street, their highest win ever in the Football League; an application for greyhound racing at Filbert Street during the summer months was rejected; a record breaking 47,298 crammed into Filbert Street to watch Leicester lose against Tottenham Hotspur in the FA Cup.
a)    1928
b)    1938
c)    1948

118.    City were eliminated at the semi-final stage of the FA Cup by Liverpool; Peter Shilton joined Stoke City for £325,000; John Toshack's agreed transfer to Filbert Street was abandoned after the player failed a medical.
a)    1973
b)    1974
c)    1975

119.    No less than 10 players were signed by Micky Adams during the summer; Les Ferdinand became City's oldest debutant; the Walkers Stadium hosted the England v Serbia & Montenegro international.
a)    2003
b)    2005
c)    2007

120.    Allan Clarke left Filbert Street for Elland Road in a £165,000 deal; Leicester appeared in the FA Cup Final; Rodney Fern notched City's first goal in Division Two in over 12 years.

a)      1967
b)      1969
c)      1970

121.    Floodlights were used for the first time in a Football League game at Filbert Street; Ian McNeill scored for City after just 10 seconds, a record which stood until Matt Fryatt broke it in 2010; City won the Division Two Championship title.

a)      1950
b)      1953
c)      1957

122.    City appeared on BBC's *Match of the Day* for the first time; Frank McLintock moved to Arsenal; City won the League Cup.

a)      1964
b)      1967
c)      1968

123.    Martin O'Neill joined Glasgow Celtic; City finished eighth in the FA Premier League; Theodoros Zagorakis made his final appearance for the City.

a)      1999
b)      2000
c)      2001

124.    The old Main Stand at Filbert Street was demolished; Swindon Town beat City in a pulsating Play-off Final at Wembley; David Speedie joined the Foxes.

a)      1993
b)      1994
c)      1997

125.    Len Shipman was elected president of the Football League; the Fosse Bar was constructed at the Double Decker end of the Main Stand at Filbert Street; former City player and manager, Johnny Duncan, died.

a)      1962
b)      1964
c)      1966

# High Flying City 1919–30

Following the name change from Fosse to City, the club enjoyed one of its most successful eras culminating in recording their highest ever League finish in 1928–29 as runners-up in Division One. At the end of that season City were described by a columnist in the *Sunday Express* as: 'the best football team...who have approached nearer to the pre-war standard than any other in individuality and constructive cleverness. I attribute this largely to the influence of their Scottish captain, John Duncan, who has insisted that the way to success was by expert use of the ball than by helter-skelter methods.' This truly remarkable decade also saw the erection of the Main Stand at Filbert Street as well as the acquisition of players who would go down in Leicester folklore.

126.   Who was the first manager of Leicester City Football Club?

127.   Leicester City FC played its first Football League game against which West Midlands club in August 1919?

128.   The first victory of Leicester City FC in the Football League was a 3–2 victory against which London club?
a)   Fulham
b)   Brentford
c)   Wimbledon

129.   City lost 5-0 against Fulham at Craven Cottage in August 1919. The game was particularly memorable for Fulham's Donald Cock. Why?
a)   he made his debut aged 15 years 3 months and scored with his first kick
b)   he was sent off before the kick-off for foul and abusive language
c)   he scored a hat-trick and was sent off for fighting

130.   Name the British monarch who was introduced to the City team prior to the FA Cup tie against Chelsea at Stamford Bridge in February 1920?

131.   Who scored Leicester City's first hat-trick?

132.   Who became Leicester City's first full international when he appeared at inside-left for Scotland against England in 1920?

133.   Who did City play at Old Trafford in 1921, which it has been reported was watched by only 13 spectators, the lowest attendance ever for Football League game?

134.   Leicester legend Johnny Duncan joined City in 1922 from which Scottish club?

135.   Arthur Chandler, City's greatest ever marksmen joined City in 1923 from which London club?

136.   Which City scoring sensation took in-person congratulations from Winston Churchill for the hat-trick he scored against South Shields, when the politician visited Filbert Street in December 1923?

137.   City finished third in Division Two in 1923 with the same number of points as second placed West Ham United. Despite City being the leading goalscorers they were denied promotion by virtue of?
a)     an inferior goal difference
b)     an inferior goal average
c)     inferior away goals

138.   Who set a City club record when he scored six goals in the Christmas Day 1924 7–0 thrashing of Port Vale?

139.   In 1924–25 how many League goals did the City striking partnership of Johnny Duncan and Arthur Chandler score between them?
a)     52
b)     62
c)     72

140. In 1925, Arthur Chandler became the first City play to notch up how many consecutive appearances for the club?
a) 50
b) 100
c) 200

141. What was unusual about Cardiff City's winning goal against City in the FA Cup quarter-final tie at Ninian Park in 1925?
a) it was the first Cardiff City FA Cup goal scored by an Englishman
b) it was scored direct from a corner-kick
c) it was the first 'golden goal' in FA Cup history

142. What title did City win for the first time in 1925?

143. Peter Hodge resigned as City's manager to take over as the manager of which club?

144. Who was City's captain throughout the majority of the 1920s?

145. Who succeeded Peter Hodge as City's manager?

146. What nickname did the *Leicester Mercury* give to the City side of the 1920s?
a) The Knuts
b) The Royals
c) The Blues

147. What historical event took place on 18 September 1926 after City beat Everton 4–3 at Filbert Street?

148. Name the south coast side City slaughtered 10–0 at Filbert Street in a Division One League game in 1928?

149. What, according to legend, occurred after Arthur Chandler scored his sixth goal in City's win over Portsmouth in 1928?

150. Leicester City's reserve team chalked up a record win against Ibstock Colliery in the Leicestershire Senior Cup in 1922. What was the final score?
a) 18–0
b) 22–0
c) 24–1

151. Why did Arthur Chandler, after a seven-week lay-off with a knee injury, on his return to League action against Aston Villa in 1926 demand that both his knees should be bandaged?

152. Who scored an amazing 32 goals in 35 outings for City in 1928–29, which saw City to the runners-up spot in Division One?

153. When City finished runners-up in Division One in 1929, which club won the title?

154. Why did club directors refuse invitations for City to tour Denmark and Sweden at the end of the highly successful 1928–29?
a) for financial reasons
b) for political reasons
c) for moral reasons

# Hat-trick Heroes

Surprisingly few players have scored hat-tricks for Leicester. Can you identify the hat-trick heroes for City in the following fixtures?

155.  City v Liverpool; Filbert Street; Football League Division One; August 1972.

156.  City v Manchester United; Filbert Street; Football League Division One; April 1963.

157.  City v Ipswich Town; Filbert Street; Football League Division One; January 1974.

158.  Derby County v City; Baseball Ground; Football League Division Two; October 1982.

159.  City v Sunderland; Filbert Street; FA Premier League; March 2000.

160.  City v Southend United; Walkers Stadium; Football League Division One; December 2008.

161.  City v Dagenham & Redbridge; Walkers Stadium; FA Cup; November 2008.

162.  City v Scunthorpe United; Walkers Stadium; Football League Championship; February 2010.

163.  West Bromwich Albion v City; The Hawthorns; Football League Championship; March 2008.

164.  City v Stoke City; Walkers Stadium; Football League Championship; August 2005.

165.  Rotherham United v City; Don Valley Stadium; Carling Cup; August 2011.

# Yo-Yo Years 1930–39

Relegation, promotion, disappointment and death best sum up the City both on and off the pitch in the turbulent years leading up to the outbreak of World War Two.

166.  Who took over as club captain following the termination of Johnny Duncan's contract?

167.  Can you name the scorer of four goals for Arsenal at Filbert Street in a Football League record 6–6 draw in 1930?

168.  City striker Ernie Hine broke what with a scorching shot in a Football League game against Sunderland on Boxing Day 1930 at Filbert Street?
a)    the referees nose
b)    the net
c)    crossbar

169.  Why was City goalkeeper Jack Beby placed on the transfer list during the 1930–31 campaign?
a)    for conceding six goals against Arsenal and five goals against Blackpool in consecutive matches
b)    on 'health grounds'
c)    for disagreeing with the coaching staff and refusing to attend training sessions

170.  In January 1932 against Crook Town in the FA Cup, who became the third City player to score five goals in a match?

171.  The City team arrived badly shaken after an incident on the journey to the Football League game at Grimsby Town in 1931–32 which they lost 0–3. What happened?
a)    City's charabanc was involved in a head-on-collision with a hearse just outside Nottingham

b)   City's railway carriage was involved in a crash whilst being shunted

c)   City's aircraft had to make an emergency landing near Skegness after colliding with a flock of seagulls, which knocked out both engines

172.  Name the City manager who resigned in January 1932 after six successive League defeats?

173.  The crowd invaded the Filbert Street twice during the final League game of the 1932–33 season. What event triggered both invasions?

a)   a torrential downpour which caused the fans on the open Popular Side (East Stand) to rush for cover

b)   poor refereeing decisions

c)   lightning strikes which gave fans in the Main Stand an electric shock

174.  In October 1933 one of City's directors was sent to Stoke City to watch a fledgling outside-right. He reported back to the City board that the youngster seemed to be 'above average ability', but no further action was recommended. Can you identify the Stoke City youngster who became a footballing legend?

175.  Name the Scottish international goalkeeper, who despite conceding six goals on his City debut, including a Dixie Dean hat-trick, against Everton in 1933 went on to make 102 consecutive appearances for Leicester?

176.  In an unsavoury encounter between City and Wolverhampton Wanderers at Filbert Street in April 1934, one of the linesmen was knocked unconscious by?

a)   a spectator

b)   a 'stray' ball after the half-time whistle had blown

c)   a Wolverhampton Wanderers official

177.   City reached the semi-finals of the FA Cup for the first time in 1934.
a)     Who were City's opponents?
b)     Where was the game played?
c)     What was the final score?
d)     Which City player faced two of his brothers in the match?

178.   Name the City manager who was admitted to Perth Infirmary on 30 July 1934 suffering from an internal compliant and sadly died three weeks later?

179.   The City board persuaded who to retire from the playing staff and take over the role of manager on the untimely death of the club's boss in 1934?

180.   What was unusual about City's friendly away game at Coventry in May 1935?
a)     two referees and two linesmen officiated the game in a FA experiment
b)     one referee and four linesmen officiated the game in a FA experiment
c)     the managers refereed the game

181.   Which former player returned to haunt City when he scored a hat-trick for Barnsley in the 3–3 draw in December 1935?

182.   Why did the *Leicester Evening Mail* on 5 March 1936 report, 'Leicester City last night selected their team for their probable home match at Filbert Street on Saturday, with opponents yet to be announced'?

183.   Filbert Street staged a special challenge tennis match between Fred Perry and Ellsworth Vines in July 1936 to raise funds to buy new players. True or False?

184.   City won promotion to Division One in 1937 thanks mainly to the remarkable efforts of which striker, signed for a then club record fee of £7,500 from Derby County, who netted 33 goals in just 27 outings?

185. Who managed City to the Division Two Championship in 1937?

186. Who slaughtered City 10–1 in a Division One game in 1938? The same club also inflicted Wembley heartbreak on City a decade or so later.

187. What did City players have on their shirts for the first time in 1939?

188. Name the Welsh right-winger, sixth on City's all-time list for League appearances, who was the first player at Filbert Street to be automatically conscripted after the outbreak of World War Two?

189. Who resigned as manager in May 1939 while the club were firmly entrenched at the bottom of Division One?

190. How many League games did City play in the 1939–40?
a)    3
b)    33
c)    43

# Foul Football

Leicester Fosse/City has had a long reputation for fair football. Bookings, dismissals, suspensions and fines have, however, accrued against the club and its players since League and Cup football began. How much do you know about Leicester's foul footballers and those who have fouled them?

191.    Leicester Fosse were fined £50 by the FA in 1898 for?
a)      poaching a player
b)      bribing an umpire
c)      postponing a game at the last minute

192.    Why were half a dozen Fosse players suspended indefinitely by the club in 1898?
a)      improper behaviour toward female relatives of Fosse Committee members at the end of season Grand Ball
b)      indiscipline and insubordination
c)      smoking cannabis

193.    Goalkeeper Jack Beby was fined by City after exchanging blows with teammate Billy Jackson in the dressing room before a reserve team game at Brentford in November 1931. What was the dispute over?
a)      a card game played on the train journey to the match
b)      the allocation of pegs in the dressing room
c)      who's turn it was to make the pre-match cup of tea

194.    Why were both the Fosse and Bolton Wanderers fined 1 guinea after the League game played at Filbert Street in 1904?
a)      the players wore shorts that were too short
b)      the players were 'scruffy'
c)      the players used 'un-gentlemanly language'

195.    Why were six Fosse players each fined £5 after losing a Football League game 4-0 at Grimsby, which was played in appalling conditions of rain, sleet and a gale force wind?

a)      for not trying
b)      for fighting among themselves after Grimsby scored their second goal
c)      leaving the field to seek shelter in the dressing room

196.    Whose City contract was terminated when he took over the licence of a public house on Welford Road in 1930?

197.    Why was City manager, Frank Womack and five of the club's directors suspended from football by the FA for 12 months in 1940?

198.    Which member of the 1949 FA Cup Final losing side published allegations of match fixing concerning City's victory over Cardiff City in the last match of the 1948–49 season which ensured the club's Division Two survival?

199.    City inside-forward, Johnny Morris was sent off in a public practice match in August 1957 and received a two week ban. What was his crime?
a)      he punched an opponent
b)      he suggested that the referee should get some spectacles
c)      he had a slanging match with his wife who was in the crowd

200.    Can you name the legendary City goalkeeper who was transfer-listed in June 1964 following an unauthorised outburst to the press?

201.    Which former City player had a 10-year ban imposed on him for 'bringing the game into disrepute' after signing a contract with the United Emirates in secret while being England's manager?

202.    Which midfield star of the Bloomfield era refused to take the field for the second half of the home League game against Ipswich in December 1974 over a dispute with the club and was fined two weeks wages and placed on the transfer list?

203. Why was City's promotion to Division One in 1983 the subject of a Football League enquiry?

204. Which City villain was unwise in his dealing with a London cabbie in the 1990s while skipper of Chelsea?

205. Name the controversial snooker player who was arrested for fighting at the end of the Grand Ball held in November 1991 to mark the Foxes centenary at Filbert Street?

206. Name the European Cup winner who was axed as City's captain after a bust-up with Martin O'Neill.

207. Which former Fox received a lengthy suspension when he made 'contact' with the referee while on loan from Chelsea to West Bromwich Albion in the early 1990s?

208. What did Robbie Fowler of Liverpool reveal to Leicester fans in 1995 that resulted in him being fined £1,000 by the FA?

209. Why were City players Tony Cottee and Andrew Impey charged with misconduct in September 1999?

210. Who left City on a free transfer after a serious and well-publicised dispute with Trevor Benjamin during a reserve team fixture?

211. Who was fined £10,000 for using the referee's toilet during the half-time break of a FA Premier League match at Filbert Street during the 2001–02 season?

212. Which players were involved in the infamous La Manga incident in 2004?

213. Which former 'Crazy Gang' member had his £30,000-a-week contract with City terminated in August 2002 after fracturing the cheekbone of a teammate during a pre-season tour of Finland?

214. What unenviable first-at-Filbert Street 'event' happened to David Walker during a League match against Clapham Orient in 1911?

215. How many Leicester Fosse players were sent-off?
a)    6
b)    8
c)    12

216. Who holds the unenviable distinction of being City's most red-carded player of all-time?

217. Who was the first City player to have been sent-off in a Football League Cup tie?

218. Who was the first City player to be sent off twice?

219. City were relegated from Division One after defeat at the Goldstone Ground, Brighton on Easter Monday 1981 in which two Leicester players were sent off. One of them was Kevin MacDonald. The other was a striker City had purchased from Oldham Athletic two years earlier. Who was he?

220. Which Scottish City midfielder was dismissed at Ibrox during a 1984 'friendly' clash with Glasgow Rangers?

221. Why was Steve Walsh forced to miss 11 matches through suspension during the 1987–88 season?

222. Steve Walsh and which other City defender, a Northern Irish international, were sent-off in a FA Cup tie against Millwall in 1991?

223. Only two City substitutes have been sent off. Colin Gibson is one, can you name the other?

224. Who is the only City player to have been red-carded in a European competition?

225. Name the former City goalkeeper who was sent off for the first time in his career in his 971st League game?

226. Who was City's first goalkeeper to be red-carded, a victim of the new 'professional foul' rules when conceding a penalty to Charlton Athletic in March 1991?

227. Which City villain-turned-hero was red-carded along with Eric Nixon after a flare-up in the last minute of the Division One Play-off semi-final against Tranmere Rovers at Filbert Street in 1994?

228. City's initial FA Premier League season of 1994–95 saw the highest number of players sent-off in one season. How many City players were red-carded that season?
a) 6
b) 8
c) 10

229. How many times was Neil Lennon red-carded while playing for City?

230. Who was sent-off for Scotland against the Faroe Islands in 1999 – which earned him a five-game international ban?

231. Which Tottenham Hotspur player was dismissed after striking Robbie Savage during the 1999 Worthington Cup Final?

232. Name the Tranmere Rovers player red-carded in the 2000 Worthington Cup Final for flooring Emile Heskey from behind after the striker had turned him on the edge of the penalty box?

233. Which Aussie had two red cards rescinded in 2007–08 season?

234. Only one City player was one red carded in 2008–09. Can you name him?

235.  Which forward, who formed a feared strike force with Lineker, when booked for the first and only time in 217 games for City, when the referee reached for his notebook apparently sighed, 'There goes my disciplinary record'?

236.  Which Leicester born striker was sent off after only 18 minutes on his City debut on the opening day of the 2004–05 season against West Ham United?

237.  Three City players were red carded in 2009–10. How many can you identify?

238.  Who was red carded during his first League start after joining Leicester on loan from Benfica during City's humiliating 6–1 loss against Portsmouth at Fratton Park on 10 September 2010?

239.  Which former City player holds the Football League record for the fastest red card, when he was dismissed after just 13 seconds, while playing for Sheffield Wednesday against Wolverhampton Wanderers on 12 August 2000?

240.  Name the City striker sent off just 11 minutes into the 2011–12 season at Coventry?

# Wartime City and the 1940s City

War and Wembley sum up City in the 1940s. As with previous decades, the 1940s is crammed full of fascinating incidents and bizarre events.

241.   Name the former City captain, later to become the club's manager, who was a founder committee member of the City Supporters' Club in 1940?

242.   Who managed City throughout the majority of World War Two?

243.   In the 1940–41 season City reached the semi-final of the League War Cup. Which club, with a highly appropriate nickname considering the circumstances, beat them?

244.   How were the 1940–41 Football League final League positions worked out?
a)   percentage of games won
b)   points (1 for a win, 0 for a draw and loss)
c)   goal average

245.   Which Championship title did City win in 1941?
a)   Football League Southern Division
b)   Football League Midlands Division
c)   Football League Northern Division

246.   Which legendary England striker played 3 games for City as a 'guest' during the 1939-40 season, scoring 5 goals?

247.   City played Northampton Town twice on Christmas Day 1941 losing 2–5 at the County Ground in the morning and winning 7–2 at Filbert Street in the afternoon. True or False?

248.   Which centre-forward, who had a 50-year association with the City, scored more wartime goals (62 goals in 81 games) for the club than any other player?

249. Which former Stoke City and Newcastle United manager, famous for signing Stanley Matthews, spent just 10 months as City's boss during the 1945–46 season.

250. The FA Cup competition was reintroduced in January 1946. What was unique about this first post-war competition?
a) only 32 clubs competed
b) all ties up to and including the sixth round were played on a two-legged basis
c) the holder had a bye until the semi-final

251. When peacetime football returned in August 1946 with the recommencement of the Football League, City had a new manager, with a familiar name. Who was he?

252. Who became City's first post-war international when he represented Wales against Ireland in April 1947?

253. In a record transfer deal in January 1948, unique in English football, no less than five City players were all transferred on the same day to which club?

254. City finished 9th in Division Two at the end of both 1946–47 and 1947–48 seasons. True or False?

255. What was the venue for the FA Cup semi-final tie between City and Portsmouth?

256. Who scored twice in City's giant-killing 3–1 win over Portsmouth in the 1949 FA Cup semi-final?

257. Who inherited the team captaincy from Sep Smith early in the 1948–49 season?

258. Which Filbert Street legend made his final appearance at the end of the 1948–49 season almost 20 years after making his debut to become the club's coach?

259. Who replaced Johnny Duncan in October 1949 as City manager and recruited Arthur Rowley from Fulham, probably the greatest-ever signing for the club?

260. What was City's average home attendance in 1948–49?
a) 25,384
b) 30,384
c) 35,384

On 30 April 1949 City played in the FA Cup Final against Wolverhampton Wanderers at Wembley.

261. How much did a 1949 FA Cup Final ticket for the Wembley North Grand Stand cost?
a) 1 shilling
b) 11 shillings
c) 21 shillings

262. The 1949 FA Cup Final was shown on television. According to the BBC at the time of the Final how many licensed sets were there in Leicestershire?
a) 35
b) 350
c) 3,500

263. Can you name both 1949 FA Cup Final managers?

264. Name both 1949 FA Cup Final captains.

265. What colour shirts did the City players wear in the 1949 FA Cup Final?

266. Which City player missed the 1949 FA Cup Final due to broken blood vessels in his nose which almost cost him his life?

267. Who wore the number-four shirt for City in the 1949 FA Cup Final and was long remembered for a 50 yard dribble past five players that ended with him scoring a Cup goal against Sheffield Wednesday in 1948?

268. Who played in goal for City during the 1949 FA Cup Final?

269. What was the half-time score in the 1949 FA Cup Final?

270. Who flicked the ball into the net after the Wolves 'keeper Williams parried Chisholm's initial effort, to score City's first-ever Wembley goal?

271. In the 64th minute of the 1949 FA Cup Final, with City losing 2–1, who fired home an equaliser from a long Harrison centre – only to see it ruled out for a debatable offside?

272. Who scored twice for Wolverhampton Wanderers in the 1949 FA Cup Final?

273. Can you name City's 1949 Cup Final centre-forward who received terrace barracking on account of his impending marriage to club chairman Len Shipman's daughter giving rise to accusations of favouritism?

274. What was the final score in the 1949 FA Cup Final?

275. Which member of the Royal Family presented the trophy to the winning captain at the end of the 1949 FA Cup Final?

# Club Connections

Apart from City which club connects the following groups of players and managers?

276.  Steve Moran – Peter Rodrigues – Dennis Rofe – Nigel Pearson

277.  Junior Lewis – Peter Taylor – Micky Adams – Ade Akinbiyi

278.  Jack Hobbs – Gary McAllister – Kevin MacDonald – Pegguy Arphexad

279.  Mike Newell – Alan Birchenall – Rodney Fern – Stefan Oakes

280.  Brian Alderson – Ken Chisholm – Tom English – Ken Keyworth

281.  Bob Hazell – Robbie James – Eddie Kelly – Frank Large – John O'Neill

282.  David Webb – Muzzy Izzet – Chris Garland – Steve Kember

283.  Alan Birchenall – Willie Carlin – Arthur Chandler – Mark Draper

284.  Allan Clarke – Matt Jones – Don Revie – Gary McAllister

285.  Ally Brown – Russell Hoult – Steve Lynex – Arthur Rowley

286.  Alan Birchenall – Mark Bright – Ally Brown – Steve Kember

287.  Iwan Roberts – Darren Eadie – Steve Walsh – Tony Cottee

288.  Martin O'Neill – Mark McGhee – Steve Guppy – Ian Andrews

289.  Mark Bright – Matt Elliott – Andy Peake – Jim Melrose

290.  Ian Banks – Stan Collymore – Ian Ormonroyd – Jimmy Quinn

291.    Brian Little – Darius Vassell – Mark Draper – Simon Grayson

292.    Gary Rowett –Yakubu Aiyegbeni – Gary Lineker – Tony Cottee

293.    Steve Howard – Phil Gee – David Nish – Peter Shilton

294.    Peter Taylor – Larry May – Simon Morgan – Alan Young

295.    Bryan Hamilton – Paul Cooper – Jamie Scowcroft – David Lowe

# 1950s City

The 1950s is best remembered for the Suez Crisis, MacMillan's 'you have never had it so good' and rock 'n' roll. But to many City fans, this was simply The Gunners' decade.

296.    What was City's highest League finish during the 1950s?
a)      18th Division One
b)      3rd Division Two
c)      6th Division Two

297.    How many different managers did City have during the 1950s?

298.    All five City forwards scored in the 1950–51 season opener, thrashing QPR 6–2 at home. True or False?

299.    City's attempt to sign Stoke City's ex-England captain Neil Franklin in the early 1950s floundered despite the clubs agreeing terms. Why?
a)      Franklin was unwilling to move
b)      Franklin failed the medical after doctors discovered he had a hole in the heart
c)      Franklin hated playing in blue

300.    Can you name the centre-half signed from Bolton Wanderers in 1952 who would later become a City legend managing the club to three Wembley Finals?

301.    A friendly between City and FK Austria during the summer of 1951 formed part of Leicester's celebrations of what?
a)      Festival of Britain
b)      Coronation of Queen Elizabeth
c)      Europe Day

302.    At the beginning of the 1951–52 season, the maximum weekly wage for City players was increased to?

a)     £14
b)     £21
c)     £48

303.   City scored 89 League goals in the 1952–53 season. How many
       came from the forward line?
a)     35
b)     55
c)     85

304.   What did City manager Norman Bullock administer to the team
       at half-time in a Division Two clash against Grimsby Town in
       November 1953, that resulted in them scoring seven second-half
       goals?
a)     cannabis
b)     oxygen
c)     caffeine tablets

305.   City won the Division Two Championship in 1954 on goal
       average, finishing just 0.03 of a goal better than which club?
a)     Manchester United
b)     Everton
c)     Wolverhampton Wanderers

306.   Who captained City to the Division Two Championship in
       1954?

307.   Name the manager who, despite winning the Division Two
       Championship in 1954, was forced to resign after an incident
       at a Whitley Bay hotel in February the following year, after a
       defeat away to Newcastle United?

308.   City achieved its highest-ever average home attendance in
       1957–58 season. How many fans on average packed into
       Filbert Street to watch the Foxes that season?
a)     20,964
b)     25,964
c)     31,359

309. City striker Andy Graver joined which East Midlands club at the end of the 1954–55 season for a then club record outgoing fee of £26,000?

310. Who became City's manager in 1955 having just guided Aberdeen to the Scottish League title?

311. Name the Scottish striker, signed from Rangers, who achieved the barely credible feat of toppling Arthur Rowley from the top of the club's scoring list in 1955–56.

312. City players, Stan Milburn and Jack Froggatt achieved what footballing feat, which has never been repeated, in a League match against Chelsea in 1955?

313. Which 'Busby Babe' signed for City for £6,500 in 1957?

314. City scored 91 goals in the 1957–58 Division One campaign. How many did they concede?
a)    47
b)    67
c)    112

315. Name the German side City played a friendly against in 1957 at Filbert Street when the floodlights were used for the first time?
a)    Mainz
b)    Borussia Dortmund
c)    Cologne

316. What was the remarkable final score in City's Division One encounter with Manchester City on 22 February 1958?
a)    Leicester City 6 – Manchester City 5
b)    Leicester City 8 – Manchester City 4
c)    Leicester City 9 – Manchester City 3

317. City paid which club £7,000 in 1959 for the services of Gordon Banks?

318. Who were the visitors in March 1959 when Filbert Street hosted its first-ever all-floodlit League game?

319. Who scored the winning goals in both the finals of the 1953 Coronation Cup as well as playing in the 1955 Scottish Cup Final for Celtic and was City's leading goalscorer in the 1958–59 season?

320. City beat the League runners-up in the penultimate game of the 1958–59 season to maintain top flight football. Who did they beat in front of 38,466 fans at Filbert Street?

# The Gunner

The next set of questions are devoted to a goalscoring phenomenon with a lethal and explosive left foot, Arthur Rowley, known to adoring City fans in the 1950s as The Gunner.

321. Arthur Rowley joined City for a fee of £14,000 in 1950 from which London club?

322. There was much criticism from City fans originally towards manager Norman Bullock on signing the relatively unproven Arthur Rowley. Why?

323. What number City shirt did Arthur Rowley wear?

324. How many full England International caps did Arthur Rowley win?

325. How many consecutive games did Arthur Rowley score for City during the 1951–52 campaign?

326. Arthur Rowley in his first season at City scored the winning goal at Hull City in 1950. Which former City star was on emergency duty between the sticks after an injury to the Tiger's 'keeper?
a) Arthur Chandler
b) Don Revie
c) Johnny Duncan

327. In his second season at Filbert Street, Arthur Rowley netted 38 times to break whose club record for the most goals in a season?

328. How many goals did Arthur Rowley score for City in the 1956–57 season?
a) 34
b) 44
c) 54

329.   Arthur Rowley holds the record for the most goals in the history of English League football. How many goals did he score in a career which spanned 619 League games?
a)   404
b)   414
c)   434

330.   Only six City players have scored 100 or more goals for the City. Gary Lineker took 207, while Arthur Chandler took 140 games to reach this milestone. How many games did it take The Gunner?
a)   92
b)   122
c)   152

331.   Whose decision to sell Arthur Rowley in the summer of 1958, as he was just eight goals short of Arthur Chandler's club record for the all-time top goalscorer, led to a loss of faith by the fans and ultimately his sacking two months into the 1958–59 season?

332.   In his eight seasons at Filbert Street The Gunner scored 265 goals in 321 games, including how many hat-tricks?
a)   8
b)   16
c)   24

333.   Can you name the striking partner of Arthur Rowley, signed from Rangers, who notched a foursome and two hat-tricks in three consecutive City home games during the 1955–56 campaign?

334.   Arthur Rowley left to become player-manager at which club, in the newly created Division Four for a fee of just £4,250?

335.   The Gunner represented Shropshire in three Minor Counties Championship matches between 1961 and 1962 as a right-handed batsman and a leg-break bowler. True or False?

# Pools Panel

What was the score in the following famous City games?

336.  City v Portsmouth; Football League Division One; Filbert Street;
      October 1928
a)    10–0
b)    0–10
c)    5–5

337.  City v Glenavon; European Cup Winners Cup, Round 1 1st leg;
      Filbert Street; September 1961
a)    1–2
b)    2-0
c)    3-1

338.  Stoke City v City; Football League Final 1st leg; Victoria Ground;
      April 1964
a)    0–0
b)    1–1
c)    2–2

339.  City v Arsenal; Football League Division One; Filbert Street; April 1930
a)    6–6
b)    7–7
c)    8–8

340.  Nottingham Forest v City; Football League Division One; City
      Ground; April 1909
a)    8–0
b)    10–0
c)    12–0

341.  Sheffield Wednesday v City; Coca-Cola Cup Round 3;
      Hillsborough; October 1992
a)    1–7
b)    7–1
c)    4–3

342.  City v Shrewsbury Town; FA Cup Quarter-Final; Filbert Street;
      March 1982
a)    4-3
b)    4-2
c)    5–2

343.  City v Harlow Town; FA Cup Round 3; Filbert Street; January
      1980
a)    0–0
b)    1–1
c)    2–2

344.  City v Wycombe Wanderers; FA Cup Round 6; Filbert Street;
      March 2001
a)    0–1
b)    1–2
c)    1–3

345.  City v Tottenham Hotspur; FA Cup Semi-Final; Villa Park; April
      1982
a)    0–1
b)    0–2
c)    1–3

346.  City v Red Star Belgrade; UEFA Cup Round 1 1st leg; Filbert
      Street; September 2000
a)    1–1
b)    1–2
c)    2–1

347.  City v Cambridge United; Football League Division One Play-off
      semi-final second leg; Filbert Street; May 1992
a)    3–0
b)    4–0
c)    5–0

348.  Leatherhead v City; FA Cup Round 3; Filbert Street; January
      1975

a)      0–1
b)      2–2
c)      3–2

349.    City v Liverpool; FA Cup semi-final; Old Trafford; March 1974
a)      0–0
b)      1–1
c)      1–3

350.    Athletico Madrid v City; UEFA Cup Round 1 1st leg; Madrid;
        September 1997
a)      1–0
b)      0–1
c)      2–1

351.    Derby County v City; FA Premier League; Pride Park, April 1998
a)      4–0
b)      0–4
c)      4–4

352.    City v Bolton Wanderers; FA Premier League; Filbert Street;
        August 2001
a)      5–0
b)      0–5
c)      5–5

353.    Liverpool v City; Football League Division One; Anfield; January
        1981
a)      0–1
b)      0–2
c)      1–2

354.    City v West Bromwich Albion; FA Cup semi-final; Hillsborough;
        March 1969
a)      1–0
b)      0–1
c)      2–0

355.  City v Manchester United; Coca-Cola Cup Round 4; Filbert
      Street; November 1996
a)    0–1
b)    1–2
c)    2–0

# Retired but Not Forgotten

Can you identify the former City players from the following snippets of information?

356.  He skippered Southampton to FA Cup glory in 1976 and ran pubs before setting up a soccer school in Tenby.

357.  He has worked as a football television pundit for Sky Sports since his retirement, as well as co-presenting 606 on BBC Radio 5 Live and in 2009 invented a unique percussion instrument that he called 'The Dube'.

358.  Last played in the Football League during the 2004–05 season with Brentford and has since played and managed in non-League football. In 2006 his autobiography *From Prison to the FA Premier League* was published.

359.  He is an East London born Turkish international whose football career was ended by injury and currently runs a Soccer Academy with former Foxes teammate Steve Walsh.

360.  England Under-23 international goalkeeper who played 400 games between the sticks for Leicester City. He worked for many years as a PE teacher in Sleaford.

361.  Signed for Leicester City by Jock Wallace he quickly became a terrace legend at Filbert Street. Plagued with injuries during the twilight of his career, he has recently turned to broadcasting and was the summariser for the BBC Radio Leicester's commentary team throughout 2011–12.

362.  A goalscoring England Under-21 international who was plucked from non-League football by Derby County in 1971. The following 12 years included spells in Belgium and America. In 2009 he was unveiled as BBC Radio Derby's match summariser for Derby County games.

363. Retired in 1975 after playing 532 League games scoring 219 goals together with 43 Northern Ireland caps. He won a League Cup winners tankard at Wembley in 1974 and a UEFA Cup runners'-up medal in 1972, while playing for Wolverhampton Wanderers. He died on 24 June 2007 at the age of 69.

364. A skillful striker who won 4 England caps. He ended his career in the States settling in Seattle where he owned a coffee shop and then drove a massive television outside broadcast lorry for an American TV company until his death from cancer in November 2004.

365. Former City winger, who became a publican in Kibworth, Leicestershire before turning into an Arthur Daley style buyer and seller. He was sent to prison for three and a half years in 2004 for laundering cannabis money.

366. He runs an events company with former England rugby player Neil Back. He also writes a column for the *Leicester Mercury*, and still attends Leicester City games on a regular basis.

367. Sadly died in 1989 aged only 33, while playing in Spain with Rayo Vallencano. He won six England caps and in 1979 moved from West Bromwich Albion to Real Madrid, for the then staggering sum of one million pounds.

368. He was given the job of manager at Leicester City on a caretaker basis following the sacking of Peter Taylor and in 2010 was appointed first team coach at Celtic.

369. Served Leicester well during his 15 years at the club playing 260 games, before becoming a prison officer.

370. City legend and a cricket all rounder jailed in February 1993 after using Post Office funds to pay off serious gambling debts.

# Swinging 60s City

Five Finals and Europe, yet another remarkable decade in the fascinating history of Leicester City. This set of questions will test your knowledge of the City throughout the swinging 60s.

371.    How many times were City promoted during the 1960s?

372.    What was City's highest League finish during the 1960s?
a)      4th Division One
b)      6th Division One
c)      10th Division One

373.    City beat West Bromwich Albion 2–1 in a fifth round FA Cup tie at Filbert Street in 1960. West Bromwich Albion's goalkeeper that day was appointed City's manager nearly two decades later. Can you name him?

374.    What was significant about City's FA Cup fifth round tie against West Bromwich Albion at Filbert Street in February 1960?
a)      it was the first time that City had reached the fifth round since 1949
b)      it was Filbert Street's first ever all-ticket game
c)      it was City's 500th FA Cup tie

375.    Can you name the left-back who from April 1960 to the end of February 1964 never missed a match for City, shattering the then club record of 194 consecutive League and Cup appearances?

376.    Thanks in part to a penalty save by Gordon Banks, City managed at the 18th attempt to record a victory at which London ground in the second Football League game of the 1960–61 season?
a)      Stamford Bridge
b)      White Hart Lane
c)      Highbury

377. Who claimed the League Cup's inaugural hat-trick in City's first round win over Mansfield Town in 1960?

378. Which club beat City in September 1960 in their record breaking opening sequence of 11 successive victories in Division One?

379. Why was the 1961 fourth round FA Cup tie between City and Bristol City at Filbert Street abandoned at half-time?
a) floodlight failure
b) quagmire of a pitch
c) death of the referee

380. Which non-League club did City overcome on the Road to Wembley in 1961?

381. It took three meetings for City to overcome Sheffield United in the 1961 FA Cup semi-final. Which three grounds staged the epic Cup tie, which after two goalless draws, City eventually won 2–0?

Leicester reached Wembley for the second time in the club's history, playing crowned League Champions Tottenham Hotspur in the FA Cup Final.

382. Name the City captain who led the side out in the 1961 FA Cup Final against Tottenham Hotspur?

383. Who was the only local-born player in City's 1961 FA Cup Final side?

384. Whose challenge in the 19th minute of the 1961 FA Cup Final gave Len Chalmers a crippling leg injury that effectively left City with 10 men?

385. Who was the manager of Tottenham Hotspur when they beat City in the 1961 FA Cup Final to win the first League and Cup double of the 20th century?

386. Who was the Tottenham Hotspur captain when they beat City 2–0 in the 1961 FA Cup Final to clinch the League and Cup double?

387. Who scored in every round of the 1960–61 FA Cup campaign for City apart from the Final?

388. Who was at the centre of a major City controversy when chosen by Matt Gillies to wear the number-nine shirt in the 1961 FA Cup Final in preference to Ken Leek, despite having played just seven games?

389. Why did Gordon Banks arrive at Filbert Street for the second round first leg European Cup-Winners' tie against Athletico Madrid just 40 minutes before kick-off?

390. What restricted the number of appearances David Gibson could make in his first season for City having been purchased from Hibernian for £25,000 in January 1962?

391. City were knocked out of the 1961–62 League Cup competition at the fourth round stage by the then Division Four side nicknamed the Minstermen. Can you identify the giant killers?

392. How did City earn their tabloid tag of 'Ice Age Champs' during the winter of 1963?

393. How did City manage to play most of their home fixtures during the winter of 1963, one of the severest winters of the 20th century, while other clubs had to postpone their games?

394. A crowd of over 37,000 watched City's 4–3 win over Manchester United in April 1963, which is thought by many to be one of the greatest games ever staged at Filbert Street. Can you name the two players who scored hat-tricks in the match?

City reached the FA Cup Final again in 1963.

395.   Who did City beat 1–0 at Hillsborough to book their place in the 1963 FA Cup Final and who scored the decisive goal, a bullet header scored after 18 minutes?

396.   Who were slight favourites to win the FA Cup Final in 1963; City or United?

397.   What colour shirts did City wear in the 1963 FA Cup Final?

398.   City's starting line-up for the 1963 FA Cup Final is given below. There are two players missing, can you identify them?

Banks

| Right | | Left |
|-------|---|------|
| Norman | | a)? |
| Appleton | King | McLintock? |
| Gibson | | Cross |
| b)? | Keyworth | Riley |

399.   City's starting line up for the 1963 FA Cup Final contained two Leicester-born players. Can you name them?

400.   Can you name both captains in the 1963 FA Cup Final?

401.   Why did City have to change their strip for the 1963 FA Cup Final against Manchester United?

402.   What was the half-time score in the 1963 FA Cup Final?

403.   Name City's scorer in the 1963 FA Cup Final 3–1 defeat against Manchester United?

404.   Who scored Manchester United's goals in the 1963 FA Cup Final?

405.   City made a profit of nearly £20,000 at the end of the 1962–63 season. How did the club invest this money?

a) a new communal bath and shower facilities for the home dressing room

b) reroofed the Double Decker and re-terraced the Enclosure

c) the whole of the Filbert Street ground was repainted

406. True or False? City headed the first published table of Division One in the 1963–64 season.

407. City were knocked out of the FA Cup in the third round in 1963, with a surprise 2–3 home defeat by Leyton Orient. The scorer of two of Orient's goals became City's coach under Frank O'Farrell at Filbert Street a few years later. Can you name him?

City reached the League Cup Final for the first time in the club's history in 1964.

408. In what year did City first play in the League Cup competition?

409. Who did City beat in the semi-final of the League Cup in 1964?

410. Where was the semi-final played?

411. The League Cup Final against Stoke City was played over two legs. What was the score at the end of the first leg played at the Victoria Ground?

412. City beat Stoke City 4–3 on aggregate to win their first major domestic trophy. Which player scored in both legs?

413. Who skippered City to League Cup glory in 1964?

City reached the 1965 League Cup Final to play Chelsea over two legs.

414. Which Midland's rivals did City demolish 8–1 away (a club record) on their way to the 1965 League Cup Final?

415. Who did City beat over two legs to reach the 1965 League Cup Final?

416. Who managed Chelsea to the 1965 League Cup Final?
a)   Ron Greenwood
b)   Tommy Docherty
c)   Bill Shankly

417. What was the score at the end of the first leg of the 1965 League Cup Final?
a)   Chelsea 2–1 City
b)   Chelsea 3–1 City
c)   Chelsea 3–2 City

418. The captain of Chelsea in the 1965 League Cup Final later became England's manager. Can you name him?

419. Who skippered City in the 1965 League Cup Final?

420. What was the final aggregate score in the 1965 League Cup Final?
a)   Chelsea 2–1 City
b)   Chelsea 3–2 City
c)   Chelsea 4–2 City

421. Name the charismatic former chairman of the PFA, author and TV pundit who led City's line in the mid-1960s with Jackie Sinclair.

422. What was unusual about the hat-trick Graham Cross scored in the City v Nottingham Forest League game played at Filbert Street in 1966?

423. Who is the only City player to have netted two own-goals in one game – to the credit of West Bromwich Albion – in April 1966?

424. Which classy City star moved to Arsenal in October 1964 for a then record incoming fee of £80,000?

425. Who wore the number-four shirt for City throughout the mid and late 1960s and aged 43 played in goal for Wrexham against Worcester City in a Welsh Cup tie?

426. Who was City's leading goalscorer for three consecutive seasons during the 1960s?

427. Name the goalkeeper who scored from a clearance in City's 5–1 victory over Southampton at the Dell in October 1966?

428. Where did Gordon Banks move to on leaving City for £52,000 in 1967?

429. Name the player signed by Matt Gillies for City in 1967 for a then record fee for a winger of £80,000, who played in the 1969 FA Cup Final, the 1971 Division Two Championship winning side and scored in the 1974 FA Cup semi-final against Liverpool.

430. In what year did Matt Gillies resign as City's manager?

431. Which club did Matt Gillies go on to manage after City?

432. Frank O'Farrell joined City from which Division Three club?

433. What was the highest League position City finished under O'Farrell's leadership?
a) 19th Division One
b) 21st Division One
b) 2nd (runners-up) Division Two

434. City required a victory in the final League game of the 1968-9 season to avoid relegation. Which United beat City to end Leicester's longest ever spell in top flight football?

435. Why did the *Leicester Mercury* threaten in 1969 a dramatic reduction in press coverage of City's games?

# Managers as Players

Many former City managers have had colourful and interesting careers as players. How many bosses can you identify from their successes or misdemeanours as players?

436.	This manager wrote himself into the history books, for all the wrong reasons, when he was sent off for dissent for Southampton on 19 August 1992 against Queen's Park Rangers at Loftus Road, during the second game of the season. His was the first ever red card in the FA Premier League. Can you name him?

437.	Who was once given a 12-game ban after punching, and breaking the nose of Hearts teammate Graeme Hogg during a pre-season friendly against Raith Rovers?

438.	This former City boss won 9 full international caps for Ireland and played for both West Ham United and Preston North End during the 1950s and 1960s. Can you identify him?

439.	In 2007 which former Foxes boss was named as one of the 12 founder members of the Aston Villa Hall of Fame?

440.	Which legendary manager had an unremarkable playing career playing as a right-back in the lower divisions of Swedish football?

441.	Whose uncle tackled Len Chalmers in the 1961 FA Cup Final which left him unable to move, which effectively ended City's hopes of winning the game?

442.	Which former manager was a member of the Portuguese 'Golden Generation' who won the UEFA Champions League in 1996 and 1997 playing for Juventus and Borussia Dortmund, respectively?

443.	Name the former City manager who won the Scottish PFA Player's Player of the Year in 1982 as well as 4 caps and 2 goals for the Scotland.

444. After scoring 50 goals in 153 appearances for Manchester United, which former boss was transferred to City in 1925, where he netted over 100 times and was part of the side that finished League runners-up in 1928–29?

445. In the FA Cup semi-final of 1977, full-time was looming in the clash between Everton and local rivals Liverpool at Old Trafford, with the score at 2–2, this former City boss put the ball into the back of the net. However, infamously, his goal which should have stood and sent Everton to Wembley was disallowed by referee Clive Thomas and the match went to a replay, which Everton lost 3–0. Who was the unlucky goalscorer?

446. During his time as a player with Crystal Palace in the 1970s, this City manager became one of the few players to have been selected for the senior England team when not playing in the top two flights of a domestic League. Can you identify him?

447. Which former boss won runners-up medals in both the FA and League Cup Finals in 1993 while playing for Sheffield Wednesday?

448. Which City manager was signed by Nottingham Forest in 1984, only for Brian Clough to decide 'he couldn't trap a bag of cement' and in his five months at the City Ground did not make a single first-team appearance before being sold to Newcastle United?

449. Which legendary Fox, best remembered for his playing career, captaining Arsenal to the League and Cup double in 1971, never quite made it as a manager?

450. Can you name the former City boss who won two European Cup winners' medals with Nottingham Forest?

# 1969 FA Cup Final

In 1969 City reached the FA Cup Final for the fourth time.

451.   How many sides did City beat to reach the 1969 FA Cup Final?
a)     5
b)     6
c)     7

452.   City beat Chesterfield Town away from home in the quarter-finals. True or False?

453.   On the day before the game Manchester City's Joe Mercer commented on the pitch, likening it to a what?
a)     cabbage patch
b)     bowling green
c)     green concrete car park

454.   Who were odds on favourites to win the 1969 FA Cup Final?

455.   How many of the 100,000 Wembley tickets were allocated to City fans?
a)     16,000
b)     24, 000
c)     32, 000

456.   As the teams prepared to leave their dressing rooms, Manchester City deliberately delayed their exit by a short period. Why?
a)     to play on any nerves Leicester players may have had
b)     the team bus broke down on the way to Wembley and they were late getting ready
c)     the clock in Manchester City's dressing room was five minutes slow

457.   City had one Welshman and two Scots in their starting line up. Can you name all three players?

458.   Manchester City coach Malcolm Allison did not take his place on the bench. Why?

a) he was on holiday with his wife having booked the trip at the beginning of the year thinking that the FA Cup Final was due to be played the previous Saturday

b) he was serving a touchline ban

c) he arrived late and was not allowed into the ground by zealous stewards who did not recognise him

459. Before kick-off, the players were introduced to the guest of honour. Who was she?

a) Princess Anne

b) Queen Banga of Tonga

c) Queen Elizabeth II

460. Three Leicester-born players were in City's 1969 FA Cup Final side. How many can you name?

461. At 21, Leicester's David Nish became the youngest ever captain of a FA Cup Final side. Can you name his opposite number who became the third oldest at 35?

462. City wore their traditional royal blue shirts, white shorts and blue socks. What strip did Manchester City wear?

463. What was the half-time score in the 1969 FA Cup Final?

464. Manchester City's goalscorer was diagnosed with terminal cancer in late 2010. Following a supporter campaign, Manchester City dedicated their FA Cup tie against the City at the Walkers Stadium, Leicester on 9 January 2011 to him. Can you name him?

465. Whose place in the City Cup Final line-up was taken by Alan Woollett after injuring his groin during a practice match against Brentford?

466. Who, once described as the 'best uncapped winger in the world', sustained an injury during the second half and was replaced by Malcolm Manley?

467. Who speared headed the attack alongside Allan Clarke and had City's best chance just after half-time when he shot high from a knock down?

468. Who was named Man of the Match by a poll of journalists?

469. Manchester City earned the right to compete in the 1969–70 European Cup Winners' Cup. City went out in the first round stage of the competition, being slaughtered 7–1 on aggregate, to Górnik Zabrze. This is still the club's worst European defeat. True of False?

470. Leicester City continued to struggle in their remaining League matches and were relegated to Division Two. Leicester became only the second club to reach the FA Cup Final and suffer relegation in the same season. By coincidence, the other club to have done so was Manchester City, who were subject to the same fate in 1926. True or False?

# Transfer Trail

Players come and players go. Can you identify the former City players from their transfer trails?

471.

| Cambridge U | Birmingham C | CITY | Wolves | Portsmouth |
|---|---|---|---|---|
| 1992 | 1994 | 1996 | 1998 | 1998 |

472.

| Walsall | Fulham | CITY | Leeds U | Barnsley |
|---|---|---|---|---|
| 1963 | 1966 | 1968 | 1969 | 1978 |

473.

| Chelsea | CITY | Birmingham C |
|---|---|---|
| 1993 | 1996 | 2004 |

474.

| CITY | Derby Co. | Tulsa Roughnecks |
|---|---|---|
| 1966 | 1972 | 1979 |

475.

| Ipswich T | CITY | Southampton | Bristol C |
|---|---|---|---|
| 1976 | 1985 | 1988 | 1991 |

476.

| CITY | Hull C | Manchester C | Sunderland |
|---|---|---|---|
| 1944 | 1949 | 1951 | 1956 |

477.

| WBA | Fulham | CITY | Shrewsbury T |
|---|---|---|---|
| 1944 | 1948 | 1950 | 1958 |

478.

| Arsenal | CITY | Vancouver Whitecaps |
|---|---|---|
| 1962 | 1971 | 1978 |

479.

| Spurs | CITY | Bolton W |
|-------|------|----------|
| 1989 | 2001 | 2005 |

480.

| Walsall | CITY | Hull C |
|---------|------|--------|
| 2003 | 2006 | 2011 |

# City in the Play-offs

At the end of the 19th century promotion and relegation issues were settled by Test Matches, involving the bottom three of Division One and the top two of Division Two. Filbert Street staged its first Test Match in 1895, when Derby County beat arch-rivals Notts County 2–1. Nearly a century later the Football League revamped the Test Match concept calling them the Divisional Play-offs. The Play-offs have provided the lowest of lows and the highest of highs for Leicester's Blue Army of fans. How much can your remember about City's roller coaster rides in the Play-offs?

481.　In what year were the promotional Play-offs introduced by the Football League?

482.　How many times have City appeared in promotional Play-off Finals?

483.　Which 6ft 4in striker scored in each of the three Divisional Play-off semi-finals City played between 1992 and 1994?

484.　City first played in the Divisional Play-offs in 1992 when they were paired against Cambridge United in the semi-final.

a)　In what position did City finish in Division Two at the end of the 1991–92 season?

b)　Can you name the manager of Cambridge United, who was the initial favourite to take over at Filbert Street after the sacking of David Pleat?

c)　Cambridge inflicted City's heaviest League defeat of the 1991–92 season. How many goals did City concede at the Abbey Stadium in September 1991?
　　　i)　4
　　　ii)　5
　　　iii)　6

d)　Which 'Rooster' scored in both legs of the semi-final?

e)　What was the aggregate score over the two legs?

485.　The 1992 Play-off Final at Wembley was between City and Blackburn Rovers, bankrolled by Jack Walker's millions.

a) Who in May 1992 became the first captain for 23 years to lead a City team out at Wembley?

b) Who was the manager of Blackburn Rovers?

c) Blackburn Rovers were awarded a controversial penalty after Steve Walsh grounded which player with the slightest of challenges?

d) Which former City striker scored the winning goal from the disputed penalty-kick?

e) Name the City goalkeeper who saved a second penalty?

486. City again reached the Divisional Play-offs in 1993 after finishing sixth in Division One.

a) Who were the Division One Champions in 1993?
   i) Nottingham Forest
   ii) Crystal Palace
   iii) Middlesbrough

b) The venue for City's home leg of the 1993 Division One Play-off semi-final against Portsmouth was Nottingham Forest's City Ground. Why?

c) Can you name the Portsmouth striker who missed at least three one-on-one chances against City goalie Kevin Poole at the City Ground?

d) Who scored the only goal of the game, after a dazzling run through the heart of the Pompey defence?

e) What was the final score in the second leg at Fratton Park, which saw City through to the Play-off Final?

487. Swindon Town beat City 4–3 in the 1993 Division One Play-off Final at Wembley.

a) Who captained City to their sixth consecutive Wembley defeat?

b) Can you name Swindon's player-manager who scored in first half?

c) In 12 magical minutes City cut Swindon Town to ribbons to wipe out the 0–3 half-time deficit. Joachim and Walsh scored one each, who netted City's equaliser?

d) Who scored Swindon's winner from yet another disputed penalty?

488.	Third time lucky for City! After finishing fourth in Division One City at last managed to overcome their Wembley hoodoo to claim a place in the FA Premier League. How much do you remember about the 1994 Play-offs?

a)	The first leg of the Play-off semi-final was played at Prenton Park. The game ended 0–0 thanks to some excellent saves from City's goalie. Can you name him?

b)	Whose last act in a blue shirt was to score the winning goal against Tranmere Rovers, which sent City to the 1994 Division One Play-off Final?

c)	City beat local rivals Derby County 2–1 in the Play-off Final at Wembley. Who scored both of City's goals?

d)	Who was the first City captain to climb the famous 39 steps to the royal box at Wembley to hold silverware aloft – the Division One Play-off Trophy?

e)	Name the City defender who won the Man of the Match Trophy in the 1994 Division One Play-off Final?

489.	After just one season in the FA Premier League, City again found themselves in the Division One Play-offs the following season.

a)	Who did City play in the 1996 Play-off semi-finals?

b)	Can you name the scorer of the only goal of the two-legged semi-final?

c)	Who started in goal for City in the 1996 Division One Play-off Final at Wembley against Crystal Palace?

d)	Who led the City side out at Wembley?

e)	Who scored City's first-ever penalty at Wembley after Izzet was felled?

f)	Can you name the striker who scored Crystal Palace's equaliser?

g)	Name the giant substitute goalkeeper Martin O'Neill sent on towards the end of extra-time during the Play-off Final, in anticipation of penalties.

h)	Whose mishit shot found the top corner with just seconds remaining to send the travelling Blue Army into ecstasy and City back into the Premier League?

i)	Who was the hapless Palace 'keeper?

490. City reached the Championship Play-offs in May 2010 just one season after being promoting from League One. Their opponents in the Play-off semi-final were Cardiff City.

a) Who won the Championship title in 2009–10?

b) What is Cardiff City's nickname?

c) How many times did the City play Cardiff City during the 2009–10 season?

d) Both clubs finished the season on 76 points. True or False?

e) The first leg of the Play-off semi-final was played at the Walkers Stadium. What was the final score?

f) What was the aggregate score after 90 minutes of the second leg?

g) Which City player's audacious chip in the penalty shoot-out ended in an embarrassing disaster?

h) Can you name the on loan City player who scored a hat-trick against Nottingham Forest to send Blackpool to the Championship Play-off Final at Wembley?

# O'Neill's Arrivals Board

Football club dressing rooms at some clubs resemble a train station concourse as players arrive and players depart. Martin O'Neill gained a reputation for shrewd acquisitions from the lower Leagues as well as breathing new life into established players. Can you identify the clubs the following players left to join Martin O'Neill at Filbert Street? To help you all the clubs are listed, but beware there are more clubs than players.

a)  Neil Lennon                    Birmingham City
b)  Spencer Prior                  Blackburn Rovers
c)  Kasey Keller                   Bolton Wanderers
d)  Gerry Taggart                  Chelsea
e)  Matt Elliott                   Crewe Alexandra
f)  Tony Cottee                    Ipswich Town
g)  Ian Marshall                   Lens
h)  Pegguy Arphexad                Millwall
i)  Steve Claridge                 Manchester City
j)  Robbie Savage                  Manchester United
k)  Muzzy Izzet                    Norwich City
l)  Steve Guppy                    Oxford United
m)  Theodoros Zagorakis            PAOK
n)  Tim Flowers                    Port Vale
o)  Andrew Impey                   Selangor
                                   West Ham United

# The 70s – the Bloomfield era & Glam Football

As the country went through the three-day week, pop music went 'Glam' as did Leicester City. For City fans of a certain age, Jimmy Bloomfield's side of the early to mid-1970s was one of the greatest in the club's history. Free flowing entertaining football played by colourful characters was the Bloomfield way. After City played Luton Town off the pitch in an emphatic 4–0 away win in the FA Cup, Malcolm Allison the then Manchester City manager said, 'That was the best display of football I have seen for years', while one national newspaper journalist went as far as writing that it was 'like watching Brazil'. Weller, Worthington, Whitworth, Birchenall and the rest of 'Bloomfield's Babes' will remain forever in those with blue blood running through their hearts as Leicester Legends.

491.   What was the highest end of season League finish for City during the 1970s?
a)   5th Division One
b)   7th Division One
c)   10th Division One

492.   How many times were City relegated from the Division One during the 1970s?
a)   0
b)   1
c)   2

493.   City won the Division Two title in 1971. The old shield, won four times previously by City, had been destroyed in a fire at Coventry in 1968 and replaced by a Cup. True or False?

494.   Can you name the teenage prodigy who notched up 14 consecutive successful penalty-kicks for City until Kevin Keelan saved from him in November 1970?

495.   What controversial incident in a Football League game against Aston Villa at Filbert Street in 1970 led to the introduction of differently designed goal stanchions?

496.   Which former City player won the Manager of the Year award in 1970?

497.   Who scored the first goal of the entire Football League in 1971 with a 45 second strike for City at Huddersfield?

498.   Which former City player and manager was voted Football Writers Association Footballer of the Year award in 1971?

499.   Name the 1971 Arsenal Double winner who had two spells with City (1977–80 and 1981–83) is in the record books as the first substitute to score in a FA Cup Final?

500.   Who captained City to the Division Two Championship in 1971?

501.   Who was City's top scorer when they won the Division Two Championship in 1971?

502.   Who was granted a testimonial game at the end of the 1970–71 season?

503.   Which club did Frank O'Farrell leave City to manage in 1971?

504.   Jimmy Bloomfield replaced Frank O'Farrell. His first match in charge was the 1971 FA Charity Shield. Who did City beat to win the Charity Shield for the first and only time?

505.   Jimmy Bloomfield played over 200 games and scored more than 50 goals for which London club?

506.   Jimmy Bloomfield joined City from which club?

507.   Which member of the 1971 Arsenal double winning side became Jimmy Bloomfield's first signing for City?

508. Who left City in August 1972 to join League champions Derby County for a then British record transfer fee of £250,000?

509. Name the legendary City striker signed from Huddersfield Town in August 1972 for £70,000, having failed a medical at Liverpool?

510. Who was the first City player in the 1970s to score 20 or more League goals in season?

511. Who scored a hat-trick for City against West Bromwich Albion in December 1972?

512. Name the former City and England goalkeeper whose career was ended prematurely after badly damaging his right eye in a head-on car crash in 1972.

513. Can you name the Manchester United goalkeeper who scored a penalty against City in a League match at Old Trafford in 1973?

514. Who was signed as a straight replacement for left-back David Nish by his former boss Jimmy Bloomfield for £125,000 from Leyton Orient prior to the start of the 1972–73 season?

515. Which former striking partner of both Frank Large and Allan Clarke was bought by Jimmy Bloomfield in 1973 for £100,000 to lift some of City's scoring burden from Frank Worthington?

516. Which club did Peter Shilton leave City to join in November 1974 for a transfer fee of £325,000?

517. City conceded a penalty after just 19 seconds in August 1974, a Football League record. From the kick-off, a stray back pass by Malcolm Manley was intercepted by Steve Heighway and was brought down by Mark Wallington. Alec Lindsay scored from the spot kick. Can you identify the side City were playing?

518. Name the legendary Liverpool and Wales striker whose £160,000 transfer to City in 1974 was quashed after he failed the medical.

519. Why did the Norwich City manager John Bond make a strong attack on City's Keith Weller and even went as far as writing to all Division One and Division Two club managers asking them to blacklist him?

520. Which former England coach plundered 4 goals in Manchester City's 5–0 thrashing of City at Maine Road in January 1977?

521. How many times did Frank Worthington score 20 or more goals in a season for City?

522. Which City defender helped Leicestershire County Cricket Club to their first County Championship in 1975?

523. Which former City captain won a League Championship medal with Derby County in 1975?

524. Which City legend use to sing with Joe Cocker?

525. The capacity of Filbert Street was lowered to what value in 1975?
a)   28,000
b)   32,000
c)   34,000

526. Name the teammate of Peter Shilton's in Leicester Boy's trophy winning team of 1965 whose inspirational performances for City after signing from Arsenal in 1975 resulted in Leicester escaping from an apparently inevitable relegation from Division One.

527. Who was City's leading goalscorer in the 1975–76 season with 11 goals?

528.   Despite being City's manager for six years, Jimmy Bloomfield only signed 11 players. Chris Garland, Steve Kember, Brian Alderson, Steve Earle and Jeff Blockley are five of them; can you name the remaining six players who are all City legends?

529.   Name the Aston Villa defender who scored all four goals in a 2–2 draw against City in a League game at Filbert Street in 1976.

530.   Name the City legend who had a much publicised on-the-field kiss with Sheffield United's Tony Currie in the 1970s.

531.   The rather vocal 'Bloomfield out' minority of City fans got their way in what year?

532.   When Jimmy Bloomfield left City, what position were they in Division One?
a)   11th
b)   16th
c)   22nd

533.   Former City player Frank McLintock occupied the hot seat vacated by Jimmy Bloomfield. In his only season in charge where did City finish in Division One?
a)   20th
b)   22nd
c)   24th

534.   To many fans City's worst-ever manager, how many League games did Frank McLintock win while in charge at Filbert Street?
a)   5
b)   9
c)   10

535.   Frank McLintock signed the following players. Can you identify the clubs they left to join City?
a)   George Armstrong
b)   Billy Hughes

c)      Roger Davies
d)      Eddie Kelly
e)      Alan Waddle
f)      David Webb

536.    Two players finished the 1977–78 season as City's leading scorers in the League with just 4 goals. Can you name them?

537.    The legendary Jock Wallace left which club to manage Leicester?

538.    What unusual fitness technique was famously used by Jock Wallace?

539.    Which City striker, the club's leading goalscorer in 1975–76, moved to Roker Park in a £200,000 deal after Sunderland failed to land Frank Worthington?

540.    Which World Cup legend and star of Holland's 'total football' team of the 1970s agreed terms to move to City and be paid on a match-by-match basis, before his agent persuaded him to sign for the Spanish side Levante?

541.    Which club did Alan Birchenall leave to join City in a deal costing £45,450 plus 'Bobby Kellard'?

542.    Can you name the centre-back who made his City debut while still studying at Loughborough University, wearing borrowed yellow shorts in the 1978–79 season opener at Burnley?

543.    Who retired from City's Board of Directors in 1978 to become the first-ever Life Member of the club?

544.    Who was City's top scorer in Jock Wallace's first season in charge at Filbert Street, with just eight goals?

545.    From which club did City sign Alan Young for a equal club record fee of £250,000 in 1979?

546.  Steve Whitworth left City after a testimonial season in March 1979 to join which club for a fee of £120,000?

547.  Name the 1976 Scottish Cup winner who formed a successful striking partnership with long term school friend Alan Young, after Jock Wallace signed him in 1978 from Philadelphia Fury?

548.  How many appearances did Gary Lineker make before scoring his first City goal?

549.  Who was City's leading goalscorer for four seasons during the 1970s?

550.  What was the furthest City managed to get in the League Cup during the 1970s?
a)    2nd round
b)    4th round
c)    5th round

# Managers, Gaffers & Bosses

Statistically football managers last just two seasons at a club before either being sacked or resign. Leicester City may only have had two managers throughout the 1960s, but since the millennium have averaged a manager a season. Not all departing City managers were sacked, some walked! All you have to do is determine whether the following City bosses were dismissed or did they leave voluntarily…in other words were they Sacked or Not Sacked?

551. Matt Gillies: City's longest serving manager, taking City to the 1961 and 1963 FA Cup Finals and winning the League Cup in 1964. Sacked or Not Sacked?

552. Jock Wallace: managed City to Division Two title glory in 1980 and the FA Cup semi-finals after winning the Scottish 'treble' with Rangers on two separate occasions. Sacked or Not Sacked?

553. Peter Taylor: managed City to the top of the FA Premier League in October 2000. Sacked or Not Sacked?

554. Johnny Duncan: captained City to their highest ever League finish and managed City to their first ever FA Cup Final appearance. Sacked or Not Sacked?

555. Brian Little: managed City's first-ever FA Premier League campaign after gaining promotion at the Play-offs and is credited with 'Starting the Wave'. Sacked or Not Sacked?

556. Frank O'Farrell: took City to the FA Cup Final in 1969 and the Division Two Championship in 1971. Sacked or Not Sacked?

557. Gary Megson: won promotion to the FA Premier League in 2002 and again in 2004 with West Bromwich Albion prior to joining City. Sacked or Not Sacked?

558. Nigel Pearson: greatest win ratio of any permanent Leicester manager, who steered City to the League One title in 2009. Sacked or Not Sacked?

559.   Mark McGhee: relegated City from the FA Premier League. Sacked or Not Sacked?

560.   Jimmy Bloomfield: during his 6 year stint at Leicester he created a side of free-flowing skilful football on a shoe-string budget, and is considered one of the club's all-time great managers. Sacked or Not Sacked?

Football management is clearly not the most secure occupation. Consequently managers must be willing to travel and move regularly in order to ply their trade. Which clubs, apart from the City have the following pairs of gaffers both managed?

561.   Nigel Pearson & Peter Taylor

562.   Peter Hodge & Sven-Göran Eriksson

563.   Matt Gillies & Dave Bassett

564.   Nigel Worthington & Ian Holloway

565.   Gordon Milne & Micky Adams

566.   Jock Wallace & Mark McGhee

567.   Brian Little & Martin O'Neill

568.   Bryan Hamilton & Gordon Milne

569.   Paulo Sousa & Ian Holloway

570.   Peter Taylor & Martin O'Neill

Can you identify the former Foxes who managed the following clubs during 2011–12?

571.   Burton Albion

572.    Oldham Athletic

573.    Huddersfield Town

574.    Manchester City

575.    Charlton Athletic

576.    Port Vale

577.    Sunderland

Former Foxes, both players and bosses have reached the pinnacle of football management by taking charge of national sides. Can you identify the national bosses from the following clues?

578.    Media pundit working mainly with Euro sport, BBC Radio 5 Live, Setanta Sports and Sky Sports who managed Northern Ireland between 1994–97. Who is he?

579.    Former England caretaker manager who has also taken charge of Dartford, Southend United, Dover Athletic, Gillingham, Leicester City, Brighton & Hove Albion, Hull City, Crystal Palace, Stevenage Borough, Wycombe Wanderers and Bradford City. Who is he?

580.    Member of Scotland's 1990 World Cup squad who took over the role of national manager in 2009. Who is he?

581.    On 3 June 2008 he was officially signed to become the manager of the Mexican national team against the advice of his closest business associates who warned of 'deep divisions within the Mexican Football Federation' and an 'underlying potential xenophobia among players and fans'. Who is he?

582.    He provoked controversy in 1977 when he quit as England's manager to become coach to the United Arab Emirates, the first time a manager of the English national team had resigned from the position. Who is he?

Managers come and managers go. Some are forgotten quickly, others will be remembered forever. Can you identify the legendary managers who achieved the following 'firsts' for City.

583.    The first to lead a City side out at Wembley?

584.    The first to play and then manage City?

585.    The first to manage City twice?

586.    The first to manage a City victory at Wembley?

587.    The first to manage City to League Cup glory?

588.    The first to manage City to the Division Two Championship?

589.    The first to manage City in the FA Premier League?

590.    The first non-British City manager?

# 1980s – The Wilderness Years

Not City's most inspiring decade – which although best summed up by the word 'mediocre', had many interesting games and characters and paved the way for the success that awaited the club in the '90s. How much do you remember about City in the Wilderness Years?

591. What was the highest end of season finish for City during the 1980s?
a) 7th Division One
b) 15th Division One
c) 20th Division One

592. How many managers did City have throughout the 1980s?

593. Who was City's leading marksmen for 4 consecutive seasons during the 1980s?

594. Only one player gained a full England cap while playing for City during the 1980s. Can you name him?

595. In the early 1980s several clubs tore up their conventional playing area and replaced it with artificial surfaces. City played Football League and FA Cup ties on artificial matches at three grounds. Can you name them?

596. Which Scottish striker joined City in 1980 for an equal club record fee of £250,000?

597. Who scored the spectacular long-range strike for City – later voted number one in a poll for the club's best-ever goal – in their 2–0 victory over Liverpool during the 1980–81 season?

598. What did City achieve on 31 January 1981 which no other club had managed to do for three years?

599. Tony Kellow scored a hat-trick for which south coast side to knock City out of the FA Cup in 1981 in a fourth round replay?

600. Jock Wallace abruptly resigned from City at the end of 1981–82 season to become manager of which Scottish side?

601. Gordon Milne left which local rivals to succeed Jock Wallace as City's manager in August 1982?

602. What was unusual about City's 6–0 win over Carlisle United in a Division Two Football League game in September 1982?

603. Name City's 1983–84 Player of the Season signed from West Bromwich Albion for £60,000 who while on trial for the Irish club Sligo was confronted by a gunman to persuade him not to prolong his trial period.

604. Who established a new club record for consecutive appearances in 1982?

605. Can you name the Brummie striker signed from Alvechurch in 1982 who would forge a powerful strike partnership with Gary Lineker?

606. Gordon Milne swapped Jim Melrose for which Coventry City player in 1982?

607. How many League goals did Gary Linker score in 1982–83 season?
a) 16
b) 24
c) 26

608. City needed to win the final League game of the 1982–83 season to secure promotion.
a) Which already relegated Lancashire side were City's opponents?
b) What was the final score?
c) Were City promoted?

609. Why did City's 1982–83 season end in controversy?

610. Which 'Bloomfield Babe' returned to the club as Public Relations Officer in 1983?

611. Can you identify the goalkeeper who conceded a Trevor Christie hat-trick on his City debut against Notts County in the opening game of the 1983–84 season?

612. Which local brewer became City's shirt sponsors in 1983?

613. Can you name the Leicester legend who sadly passed away in 1984, the club's centenary year?

614. In 1984 Trevor Bennett became the club's first post-war what?
a) Vice President
b) secretary
c) doctor

615. City played their first Sunday League game in December 1983 against which local rivals?

616. Which club landmark was reached when David Rennie scored against Coventry City in the first Sunday game staged at Filbert Street in December 1984?
a) 3,000th League goal
b) 5,000th League goal
c) 7,000th League goal

617. Kevin MacDonald left Filbert Street in November 1984 to join which club for a record incoming transfer fee of £400,000?

618. What did former City striker Alan Smith lose during a match while playing for Arsenal against Stoke City in 1984, only for them to be found and returned to their rightful position after the game?

619. Who were City's Scottish opponents in the club's Centenary Game in August 1984?

620. Who became only the sixth player to score 100 League goals for City when he netted twice in the 4–3 defeat at Queen's Park Rangers on 4 May 1985?

621. From which club did City sign Gary McAllister and Ali Mauchlen in a deal worth £250,000 in 1985?

622. Can you name the former City and England full-back who scored his one and only League goal in 1985 for Mansfield Town against Hereford United in his 570th game?

623. Who succeeded Mark Wallington as City's number-one goalkeeper?

624. Which rival Midland club did Mark Wallington join after leaving City in 1985?

625. Which club did Gary Lineker leave City to join in 1985 for £800,000?

626. Name the City striker, the subject of occasional racist hostility at Filbert Street, who upon joining Crystal Palace in 1986, formed a lethal striking partnership with Ian Wright.

627. Who was brought in as City's team manager in June 1986 after Gordon Milne was given the role of general manager?

628. Can you name the Leicester legend signed from Wigan Athletic for £100,000 in June 1986?

629. Can you name the 1975 Young Footballer of the Year who moved from Southampton to City in 1986, for a then club record fee of £300,000?

630. Name the former Real Madrid and West Bromwich Albion winger who had an extended loan spell with City, which despite being injury strewn, was inspirational in keeping them in Division One in 1986.

631. Name the legendary City striker who was voted PFA and FWA Player of the Year in 1986.

632. Which Arsenal striker played for City against the Gunners in 1987?

633. Name the striker whose goal earned Finland a draw against England in 1985, who joined City in 1987 from IFK Gothenburg.

634. How many consecutive away defeats did City suffer in 1986–87?
a)     7
b)     11
c)     17

635. The club record transfer fee was broken in 1987 when which striker left Luton Town to join City?

636. City found goalscoring a struggle at times throughout 1987. How many successive games did City fail to score in 1987?

637. Which former striking partner of Gary Lineker won two Football League Championship medals, scored the winning goal in a Cup Winners' Cup Final and won a Charity Shield winners medal after leaving City in 1987?

638. Name the goalkeeper, famed for his prowess at saving spot-kicks and winner of both FA Cup and UEFA Cup winners' medals with Ipswich Town, who became City's number-one during the 1988–89 season.

639. David Pleat left which club to replace Bryan Hamilton as City's manager in 1987?

640. Name the striker who won three Scottish Premier League titles, three Scottish Cups and a European Cup Winners Cup winners medal with Aberdeen before becoming David Pleats' first signing as City boss in 1988.

# Strike Force

Can you identify current and former City marksmen from the following snippets of information?

641. He was City's top scorer for three seasons running in 1961–62, 1962–63 and 1963–64 and played in both the 1961 and 1963 FA Cup Finals, scoring Leicester's solitary goal in the latter Final. Name that striker.

642. He is often noted as the player who scored the goal which 'saved Alex Ferguson's job' in 1990. Name that striker.

643. He was Blackpool's leading scorer in their first season in the FA Premier League, with 13 goals. Name that striker.

644. He is best remembered by City fans for his hat-trick against Leicester's arch-rivals Derby County at Filbert Street in April 1994, and was described by a local Norfolk newspaper as 'one of the greatest goalscorers ever to pull on a Norwich City shirt'. Name that striker.

645. At Celtic, this Leicester born striker achieved double success, with Scottish League Cup and Scottish Premier League winner's medals. Name that striker.

646. He was a prolific goalscorer especially in his West Ham United days, where he was voted the PFA Young Player of the Year in 1986, the year the Hammers finished third (their highest League finish to date). Name that striker.

647. In the 2008–09 season he became the first City player in 42 years to score 20 goals before Christmas, and the first in 83 years to hit hat-tricks in successive matches. Name that striker.

648. He scored the first goal in Arsenal's dramatic League Championship winning victory at Anfield in May 1989, and the only goal of the 1994 European Cup-Winners' Cup Final victory

against Parma. He was Arsenal's top scorer for four consecutive seasons, and the top scorer in Division One in the 1988–89 season with 23 goals. Name that striker.

649. Under Eriksson with England, he scored 6 goals from 22 international caps awarded between 2002 and 2004, including appearances at the 2002 World Cup in Korea/Japan, and the 2004 European Championship in Portugal. Name that striker.

650. This Scottish international scored a career-high of 20 goals in the 2002–03 season as Leicester made an immediate return to the top flight, finishing runners-up in Division One behind Portsmouth. Name that striker.

651. He joined City on 31 August 2011 from Everton for £2.5 million just 40 minutes before the transfer window closed to sign a four-year contract. Name that striker.

652. He won 8 caps for England in 1974, scoring 2 goals, during his time at Leicester City. Name that striker.

653. He scored 273 goals for City. Name that striker.

654. He scored 117 goals in total for City making him the club's fourth top goalscorer of all-time, including 4 in the 6–3 victory over Aston Villa in November 1958. Name that striker.

655. After winning the League Cup in 1997 and 2000 with City, he made a big money move to Liverpool in 2000. Name that striker.

656. He has played for 15 different League clubs and several non-League football clubs, playing in over 1,000 professional or semi-professional football matches. Name that striker.

657. On 28 March 2007 he made his debut as a late substitute for England in a Euro 2008 qualifying match against Andorra in Barcelona and marked the occasion with a 93rd-minute goal. Name that striker.

658.    He failed to score for 17 games before bagging a hat-trick and assisting a goal in City's 5–1 win over Scunthorpe United on 13 February 2010, leaving the field to a standing ovation seven minutes from the final whistle. Name that striker.

659.    He joined Leicester City on 1 January 2008 for a fee of £1.5 million from Derby County, signing a three and a half year contract. Name that striker.

660.    He scored the first-ever goal in the FA Premier League for Sheffield United against Manchester United after five minutes on 15 August 1992. In the same game he scored a second after 50 minutes from the penalty spot as Sheffield United went on to win 2–1. Name that striker.

# Name that Gaffer

All the answers for the next set of questions are the men who have managed City in the 50 years from 1960.

Micky Adams
Martin Allen
Dave Bassett
Jimmy Bloomfield
Frank O'Farrell
Matt Gillies
Sven-Göran Eriksson
Bryan Hamilton
Ian Holloway
Rob Kelly
Gordon Lee
Craig Levein
Brian Little
Mark McGhee
Frank McLintock
Gary Megson
Gordon Milne
Martin O'Neill
Nigel Pearson
David Pleat
Paulo Sousa
Peter Taylor
Jock Wallace
Nigel Worthington

Which manager:

661. ...was criticised by his club chairman whilst manager of Tranmere Rovers in 2005 for not spending available cash on team strengthening?

662. ...while in charge of City he purchased no one and gave no player a debut?

663.    ...had his City contract terminated by 'mutual consent' after just 4 matches in charge?

664.    ...was the first catholic to captain Northern Ireland?

665.    ...smashed the British transfer record by signing Allan Clarke for £150,000 from Fulham in 1968?

666.    ...was replaced as manager of Manchester United by Tommy Docherty?

667.    ...succeeded Jock Wallace as City's manager?

668.    ...played in two FA Cup Finals for City and in 2009 was inducted into the English Football Hall of Fame?

669.    ...has the unique distinction of being the only player ever to play in the English, Welsh and Scottish Cup competitions in the same season.

670.    ...left City in October 2007 just 41 days and nine Football League Championship games after his appointment.

671.    ...took 21 points from a possible 30 in his first 10 games in charge of City and was awarded the Championship Manager of the Month award for March 2006?

672.    ...was part of the Aberdeen side which won the 1983 European Cup Winners' Cup and 1983 UEFA Super Cup, as well as three Scottish Premier Division titles?

673.    ...is best remembered for an often-televised clip of him running onto the pitch in 1983 to celebrate, after a last-minute goal by Raddy Antic against Manchester City prevented Luton Town from being relegated from Division One?

674.    ...was in charge for City's first game at the Walkers Stadium?

675.    ...signed Steve Walsh for City?

676.    ... managed England in the 2002 FIFA World Cup Finals

677.    ...won 51 International caps and played for his country at UEFA Euro 1996 and 2000?

678.    ...made his Scotland debut in March 1990, a 1–0 win against reigning world champions, Argentina at Hampden Park, and played well enough to earn a place in Scotland's 1990 World Cup squad?

679.    ...took City to the League One title and the Championship Play-off semi-finals?

680.    ...guided Blackpool to the FA Premier League in 2010 after winning the Play-offs following a sixth-placed finish in the Championship?

681.    ...managed Wimbledon, Watford, Sheffield United, Crystal Palace, Nottingham Forest, Barnsley and Southampton as well as City?

682.    ...won the Charity Shield with City in 1971?

683.    ...took on England coaching duties whilst managing City?

684.    ...signed Frank McLintock and sold Gordon Banks?

685.    ...was given a 5-match contract by Milan Mandaric in April 2007 to keep City in the Championship?

# Book 'em!

Footballers like all celebrities cannot resist telling their own life stories. See how many former City players and managers you can name from the title of their biography.

686.  *Stan: Tackling My Demons*

687.  *One Hump or Two?*

688.  *Starting the Wave*

689.  *Tales from the Boot Camps*

690.  *Bring Back the Birch*

691.  *The Magnificent Obsession*

692.  *Strikingly Different*

693.  *Here, There & Everywhere*

694.  *True Grit*

695.  *Revered and Reviled*

# 1969–89 Sweet FA Cup City

696.  How many times did City reach the semi-final stage of the FA Cup between 1969 and 1989?

697.  Can you name the scorer of Chelsea's winning goal in the replayed 1970 FA Cup Final, who joined City from Queen's Park Rangers in 1977?

698.  The FA Cup quarter-final tie against Arsenal in March 1971 was the last time that more than 40,000 supporters watched City at a home game. True or False?

699.  Which London side knocked City out of the FA Cup three times during the 1970s?

700.  Which City legend scored a superb individual goal against Luton Town in round four of the FA Cup in 1974, a fitting climax to a stunning team performance which drew from The Sunday Times a heartfelt comparison between Leicester's football and that of Brazil?

701.  City reached the semi-final of the FA Cup in 1974. Which club did City draw 0–0 with at Old Trafford, but sadly lost the replay 1–3 at Villa Park?

702.  Why were City classified as the away side in the FA Cup third round tie against Isthmian League Leatherhead played at Filbert Street in January 1975?

703.  Leatherhead led City by what score at half-time in a third round FA Cup tie at Filbert Street in front of Match of the Day cameras, before eventually losing 3–2?

704.  Who or what was the 'Leatherhead Lip'?

705.  How many FA Cup goals did Frank Worthington score for City?

706.    Who made his debut for Leicester at Queen's Park Rangers in March 1974 and hit the headlines for scoring two goals that took City to the semi-finals of the FA Cup?

707.    Which striker, a summariser on BBC Radio Leicester throughout 2011–12, scored a hat-trick to knock City out of the FA Cup in 1979?

708.    Which City midfield star is remembered by many fans for wearing white tights in Leicester's 3–0 third round FA Cup tie victory over Norwich City in 1979 in front of the Match of the Day cameras?

709.    Which non-League club sensationally knocked City out of the FA Cup in 1980, winning 1–0 in a third round replay at the tiny Hammarskjold Road Sports Centre?

710.    Which club, based at St James Park knocked City out of the FA Cup in 1981?

711.    How many different goalkeepers did City use in their FA Cup quarter-final win against Shrewsbury Town in 1982?

712.    Which defender broke his leg during City's 2–0 FA Cup semi-final defeat by Tottenham Hotspur at Villa Park in 1982?

713.    Despite not being suspended or injured, why was the 1982 FA Cup semi-final between City and Tottenham Hotspur at Villa Park, the last competitive game Ossie Ardiles played for some time?

714.    Who scored a spectacular own goal in City's 1982 FA Cup semi-final defeat by Tottenham Hotspur at Villa Park?

715.    Against which non-League team did City have to replay a third round FA Cup match against behind closed doors, despite having won the first tie played at the Baseball Ground 6–1?

113

# 1990s...the Glory Years

Brian Little 'Started The Wave' in 1991, which paved the way for Martin O'Neill to lead the club to glory. The 1990s was full of highs and lows, dominated by the League Cup and the two P's – Play-offs and the Premier League. How much do you remember about City's journey through the 90s?

716.     What was the highest end of season finish for City during the 1990s?

a)     7th FA Premier League

b)     9th FA Premier League

c)     12th FA Premier League

717.     City had five permanent managers during the 1990s. How many can you name?

718.     How many times did City play at Wembley during the 1990s?

719.     How many times were City promoted during the 1990s?

720.     Gary McAllister was sold to which club in 1990 for £1 million?

721.     What City 'first' is associated with the Full Members' Cup tie against Wolverhampton Wanderers in November 1990?

a)     City players had their surnames on the back of their shirts for the first time

b)     it was the first live transmission of a City home game

c)     it was the first Cup game played in England with a yellow ball

722.     Name the City chairman, who resigned after sacking David Pleat.

723.     Can you name the Leicester legend who was red-carded three times during the 1990–91 season?

724.     Who scored possibly the most important goal ever at Filbert Street when he netted the winner against Oxford United in May 1991, which ultimately proved enough to save the club from relegation to the third tier of English football for the first time in their history?

725. Despite only being manager of Leicester City for a brief period, who is fondly remembered for saving the club from relegation to the uncharted depths of the (old) Third Division following the disastrous tenure of David Pleat?

726. Brian Little managed which club to the Vauxhall Conference and the Division Four titles in successive years before becoming City's manager in June 1991?

727. Name the three former Quakers players who relocated to Leicester during 1991–92.

728. Who were Brian Little's three-man backroom?

729. Nottingham Forest beat City 2–0 in the Area Final of which Cup competition in 1991?

730. In what year did City adopt an all blue home strip?
a) 1990–91
b) 1992–93
c) 1994–95

731. Which club slaughtered City 7–1 at Hillsborough in the 1992 League Cup competition?

732. Paul Kitson became the subject of City's record outgoing transfer deal when moving to Derby County in 1992 at a cash-plus-players valuation of £1.35 million. Name the two Derby players who joined City as part of the deal.

733. Why did the mid-week Anglo-Italian Cup qualifier against West Bromwich Albion in September 1993 kick-off at 6pm?
a) an electrical cable had been severed the previous weekend and the ground only had generators capacity for the 'basics'
b) construction of the Carling Stand meant that the ground only had two floodlight pylons
c) the tie was being televised as part of a 'Wonderful Wednesday' football extravaganza on BskyB

734.    Newcastle United celebrated the capture of the 1993 Division One Championship at St James' Park by slaughtering City 7–1 in a match televised on Sky. Which former City striker collected a hat-trick to counter the one he scored for City against Newcastle two seasons earlier?

City finally secured their place in the FA Premier League after overcoming Derby County in the 1994 Division One Play-off Final. Sadly City's stay in the top flight of English football was a short one.

735.    Who was City's captain throughout the club's first-ever FA Premier League campaign?

736.    City lost their first-ever FA Premier League fixture 1–3 in a match which kicked-off at 4pm on a Sunday for the benefit of Sky Sports. Who were City's opponents that day?

737.    Who missed City's first penalty-kick in the FA Premier League, awarded in the opening game of the season?

738.    Who scored City's first FA Premier League goal?

739.    City's first win in the FA Premier League, was a 3–1 home victory over which London club?

740.    Can you name the City defender who scored consecutive own-goals in FA Premier League games against Queen's Park Rangers and Wimbledon in August/September 1994?
a)      Mike Whitlow
b)      Jimmy Willis
c)      Simon Grayson

741.    What reason did Brian Little give for resigning as City's manager in November 1994?
a)      to spend more time with his family
b)      the board of directors after they refused to give him the money to sign Brian Deane from Sheffield Wednesday for £1.2 million
c)      personal reasons

742. Who took over as City's caretaker manager for one game, a remarkable 2–1 home victory over Arsenal, following Brian Little's resignation?

743. Whose only FA Premier League goal for City, in the home victory over Arsenal in November 1994, was belatedly scrubbed from the record books after the League Panel re-assigned it as a Gunners own-goal?

744. Can you name the youth team coaches who were temporarily handed the duty of senior team selection in the wake of Brian Little and his backroom staff's resignation?

745. Brian Carey and which other City player were sent off in the FA Premier League game away at Wimbledon in 1994?

746. Who was City's manager when the club recorded its first clean sheet in the FA Premier League, a 0–0 draw against Blackburn Rovers in December 1994?

747. Mark McGhee was appointed Brian Little's successor, leaving which club to join City in 1994?

748. For how many months was Mark McGhee City's boss?

749. Which former Manchester United and Norwich City striker became City's second £1 million player in January 1995?

750. City recorded only one away win in the FA Premier League in 1994–95, a game played in atrocious weather conditions. Who did City beat?

751. In February 1995 City pulled back a 1–4 deficit, with just 13 minutes remaining, to gain a point away at which Midland rivals?

752. Name the former Parkhurst prisoner distinguishable by his 'pineapple cut' who joined City from Doncaster Rovers for £125,000 in 1995.

753. City's initial FA Premier League campaign of 1994–95 saw the highest number of players sent off in a single season in the club's history. How many players took an early bath that season?
a)   7
b)   8
c)   9

754. Which Leicester born striker made his City debut at Queen's Park Rangers in March 1995?

755. Who was City's top scorer in the club's first-ever FA Premier League campaign in 1994–95?

City now had the taste for the FA Premier League and wanted more.

756. With which former City star did Gerry Taggart grow up with in Belfast as well as joining him as a trainee at Manchester City?

757. Mark Draper, City's first £1 million acquisition was sold to Aston Villa for how much in 1995?
a)   £2.55 million
b)   £3.25 million
c)   £4 million

758. Which Division Two side, based at the Goldstone Ground, knocked FA Premier League City out of the FA Cup in 1995?

759. Name the midfielder Brian Little signed, as Aston Villa's manager, from City in a deal worth £1.5 million.

Mark McGhee was replaced by Martin O'Neill. Under Martin O'Neill, Leicester qualified for the 1995–96 Division One Play-offs, beating Crystal Palace 2–1 with a last-second Steve Claridge goal securing an immediate return to the FA Premier League. Following promotion, Leicester established themselves in the FA Premier League with 4 successive top 10 finishes. O'Neill was the first manager to win silverware for 26 years, winning the League Cup twice. The club qualified for the UEFA Cup in 1997 and 2000, the club's first European competition since 1961. O'Neill's success made him a sought-after manager, turning down Leeds United in 1999, but in June 2000 he was persuaded to travel to Glasgow to manage Celtic. How much do you know about the O'Neill-era at Leicester?

760. Mark McGhee walked away from City to join which 'bigger club'?

761. Martin O'Neill resigned as the manager of which club just days prior to becoming City's boss?

762. What was the highest position City finished under the leadership of Martin O'Neill?
a)     8th FA Premier League
b)     10th FA Premier League
c)     12th FA Premier League

763. How many years was Martin O'Neill City's manager?

764. Name the Swedish international, regarded by many as the best man-for-man marker of his era, who joined City from IFK Gothenburg in 1995.

765. Name the two Australian players who left City at the beginning of 1996 to join Mark McGhee at Wolves in a joint deal worth around £1.8 million.

766. Name the European Cup winner who was axed as City's captain after a bust-up with Martin O'Neill.

767. City exited the FA Cup after suffering a 5-0 thrashing away from home in February 1996 against which club?

768. Name the striker who signed for City on the eve of the 1997–98 season from Blackburn Rovers for £1.1 million.

769. Who won the League Cup with Nottingham Forest in 1989 and 1990 and with City in 1997?

770. After 83 minutes City were losing 0–2 at home against Arsenal in the FA Premier League in 1997. What was the final score?

771. Who fired City into an early lead in the first leg of the 1997 UEFA Cup tie against Athletico Madrid?

772. Who was red-carded in the second leg of the UEFA Cup tie apparently for taking a free-kick too quickly?

773. Leicester City plc was floated on the Stock Exchange in 1997. How much was each share originally worth?

774. Who was appointed the first chairman of Leicester City plc in 1997?

775. Whose first FA Premier League goal for City inflicted a rare home defeat on Manchester United in January 1998?

776. Steve Claridge left City in 1998. Can you name the former City manager who signed him in a deal worth £400,000?

777. Which League did City top at the end of the 1998–99 season?

778. Which City player finished the 1998–99 campaign as the only FA Premier League player to have completed 90 minutes of every single fixture?

779. Which Northern Ireland centre-half was signed by City on a free transfer from Bolton Wanderers in 1998.

780. Who became the club's record signing when City paid just over £2 million for his services in August 1998?

781. Which City player was voted Carling FA Premier League Player of the Month in September 1999?

782. Who smashed City's transfer record when he moved from Norwich City in December 1999 for £3 million?

783.    Which much travelled striker sealed City's victory at White Hart Lane in April 1999 by scoring his 200th League goal?

City dominated the League Cup throughout the 1990s. How much can you remember?

784.    How many times did City reach the League Cup Final between 1990 and 2000?

785.    Who did City beat in a two-legged semi-final to reach the League Cup Final in 1997?

786.    Whose City debut, in the first leg of the semi-final of the League Cup 1997, lasted only 11 minutes before suffering a broken leg?

787.    Can you name Middlesbrough's manager who led his team out at Wembley to face City in the 1997 League Cup Final?

788.    Martin O'Neill gave Pontus Kåmark the task of man marking which Brazilian during the 1997 League Cup Final?

789.    City's starting line up against Middlesbrough in the 1997 League Cup Final comprised eight Englishman. Pontus Kåmark was one of the non-English players, can you name the other two?

790.    Which Italian striker scored in extra-time to break the Wembley deadlock in the 1997 League Cup Final?

791.    City equalised with how many minutes of extra-time remaining to send the Cup Final to a replay?

792.    Which ground staged the replay of the 1997 League Cup Final between City and Middlesbrough?

793.    Who scored City's goal in the 100th minute to win the League Cup in 1997?

794.  Who lifted the League Cup in 1997 and won the Man of the Match award?

795.  Which striker scored five goals for City in the 1998–99 League Cup competition?

796.  Who did City play in the 1999 League Cup Final?

797.  Who was City's captain in the 1999 League Cup Final?

798.  Which two strikers spear headed City's strike force in the 1999 League Cup Final?

799.  What was the half-time score in the 1999 League Cup Final?

800.  Who was sent off in the 1999 League Cup Final for striking Robbie Savage?

801.  Who scored the winning goal in the 1999 League Cup Final?

802.  City also reached the League Cup Final in 2000 after beating Aston Villa in the semi-final. Who was Villa's manager that day?

803.  Who were City's opponents in the 2000 League Cup Final?

804.  Which manager led the City team out at the last League Cup Final to be played at the old Wembley Stadium?

805.  Which England international appeared between the sticks for City in the 2000 League Cup Final?

806.  Who scored the first goal in the 2000 League Cup Final, from a Steve Guppy corner?

807.  Name the only City player to be booked in the 2000 League Cup Final?

808.  What was the final score in the 2000 League Cup Final?

809.   Who climbed Wembley's 39 steps to collect the League Cup in 2000?

810.   Emile Heskey holds the record for the most League Cup Final appearances (6) with which legendary Liverpool striker of the 1980s?

# Jeepers Keepers

Leicester has a long reputation for producing and signing top-class 'keepers. Can you identify past and present Leicester No.1s from the following clues?

811.   He signed a pre-contractual agreement with City before joining on 1 July 2009 when his contract with Bristol City expired.

812.   He became known for both saving and scoring penalties, most notably the winner in a shoot-out against Watford in the FA Cup in 1998.

813.   City's goalkeeper in the 1949 FA Cup Final.

814.   His final appearance for Leicester City was against Wolverhampton Wanderers at Molineux in May 2003 as a late substitute with City leading 1–0. Leicester were awarded a late penalty, and despite shouts from the travelling Foxes fans for him to take the penalty, Micky Adams ignored the fans, and allowed Trevor Benjamin to take it, who scored. It seemed harsh on the goalie as Leicester were already promoted to the FA Premier League, and he could have ended his career with his only goal.

815.   He remains the youngest goalkeeper to play for Scotland, when he made his debut aged 18 years and 152 days in 1929.

816.   He was ever-present for City in six successive seasons from 1975–81.

817.   He won six medals with Liverpool, all as an unused substitute.

818.   He was listed by Pelé as one of the 125 greatest living footballers.

819.   A Hungarian international goalie who played on loan for City during 2007.

820.   His £250,000 move to Leicester was not a great success, as he tore a stomach muscle in his first match and was out injured for

several months. He made 80 appearances in 3 years before moving to Hartlepool in the summer of 1991, where he stayed for 2 years before joining Rochdale for a season.

821. In a 30-year career, which included 11 different clubs, three World Cup Finals tournaments, two European Cup Finals and more than 1,000 competitive matches, he emerged as one of the English game's genuine legends. He has the rare distinction of having played over 100 League games for 5 different clubs.

822. A four-time World Cup Finals participant and was the first American goalkeeper to become a regular in the German Bundesliga, the FA Premier League, and the Spanish La Liga.

823. He played for Leicester in the 1992 Division Two Play-off Final against Blackburn Rovers.

824. He signed a new contract for Burton Albion in 2011 at the age of 47.

825. Standing at 2.02m, he is one of the world's tallest professional goalkeepers, who won the Champions League with AC Milan in 2007.

826. A Leicester-born goalie who played for City on loan in 2010.

827. He signed a four-year contract with City in July 2001 for a fee of £2.5 million.

828. An English amateur football player who competed in both the 1908 and 1912 Summer Olympics.

829. He joined City from Leeds United in 2011.

830. He appeared as a witness at the November 1924 inquest on the Fulham forward Harvey Darvill with whom he had collided a few weeks previously and who'd died of internal injuries after completing a couple of further Division Two games.

# Leicester or Not?

Are the following City players Leicester born and bred...in other words are they Local or Not Local?

831.  Dion Dublin: Local or Not Local?

832.  Arthur Chandler: Local or Not Local?

833.  Alan Birchenall: Local or Not Local?

834.  Johnny Duncan: Local or Not Local?

835.  Peter Shilton: Local or Not Local?

836.  Norman Plummer: Local or Not Local?

837.  Steve Walsh: Local or Not Local?

838.  Richie Wellens: Local or Not Local?

839.  Graham Cross: Local or Not Local?

840.  Bob Lee: Local or Not Local?

841.  Trevor Peake: Local or Not Local?

842.  David Nish: Local or Not Local?

843.  Gordon Banks : Local or Not Local?

844.  Don Revie: Local or Not Local?

845.  Emile Heskey: Local or Not Local?

846.  Muzzy Izzet: Local or Not Local?

847.  Gary Lineker: Local or Not Local?

848.    Keith Weller: Local or Not Local?

849.    Howard Riley: Local or Not Local?

850.    Steve Whitworth: Local or Not Local?

# Twenty-First Century City 2000–10

Within a few months of the start of the 21st century City sat proudly at the top of the FA Premier League. Unfortunately it only lasted a few hours as the City rapidly tumbled downwards until they found themselves in the third tier of English football for the first time in 2008. Within a season City were back in the Championship challenging for a place in the top flight. How much can you remember about City's turbulent first decade in a new millennium?

851.   What was the highest end of season finish for City in the first decade of the 21st century?
a)   6th FA Premier League
b)   8th FA Premier League
c)   11th FA Premier League

852.   How many different permanent managers did City have from the departure of Martin O'Neill in June 2000 to the appointment of Sven-Göran Erickson in 2010?

853.   How many seasons did City spend in the FA Premier League during the first decade of the 21st century?

854.   Who succeeded Martin O'Neill as City's manager in 2000 and which club did he leave to join Leicester?

855.   City broke the bank when they paid a whooping £5 million for the services of striker Ade Akinbiyi from which club?

856.   How many goals did Ade Akinbiyi score in his 18 month stint with City?

857.   Name Leicester's English international goalkeeper who won the Carling Player of the Month award for September 2000.

858.   What happened for the first time on 1 October 2000?
a)   City won their fourth consecutive away game in the FA Premier League.

b)     City went top of the FA Premier League.

c)     City were named Carling FA Premier League Team of the Month.

859.    As a result of winning the League Cup in 2000 City played in a European Cup competition for the third time in their history.

a)     Which former European Cup winners were City drawn against?

b)     The score at the end of the first leg at Filbert Street was 1–1. Who scored City's equaliser?

c)     Why was the second leg switched at the last minute to Vienna?

d)     What was the final aggregate score?

860.    The only away goal City conceded in their first seven matches of the 2000–01 season was scored by which Leicester-born striker?

861.    Can you identify the England striker, who would later become a Fox, who scored a hat-trick in Tottenham Hotspur's 3–0 thumping of City in the FA Premier League in November 2000?

862.    Which company replaced Walkers Crisps as City's shirt sponsors in 2000?

863.    Which recently promoted side, every bookmakers' favourites to go straight back down, handed City their worst ever opening day home defeat – a 0–5 stuffing in August 2001?

864.    Can you name the Italian footballing legend, now a FA Premier League manager, who joined City in January 2001?

865.    How many months was Peter Taylor in charge at City?

866.    Garry Parker was temporarily put in charge of City after Taylor's departure. What was the final score of Parker's only game as manager?

867.    Official statistics in November 2001 showed that 83 per cent of which City striker's attempts were 'off target' – branding him the League's worst striker?

868.  Leicester City went into administration in 2002. According to Deloitte & Touche what was the club's total debt?
a)    £25 million
b)    £50 million
c)    £100 million

869.  In mid-December 2002 Millwall visited the Walkers Stadium.
a)    Which former Fox was Millwall's manager?
b)    Before the game Alan Birchenall made what important announcement to the fans?
c)    Why were away fans banned?
d)    Which controversial former Fox, hated by the majority of City fans, was booed throughout the game?
e)    Who fired Millwall in front after just 15 seconds into the game having been given a heroes welcome by City fans?
f)    What was the final score?

870.  A vote was held at half-time in the home game against Watford in 2002 to decide whether the club should revert back to its original name, Leicester Fosse. Approximately what proportion of fans voted for the status quo?
a)    60 per cent
b)    70 per cent
c)    90 per cent

871.  Mick Adams achieved the impossible given the financial status of City by guiding them to promotion to the FA Premier League, setting many club records along the way. How many defeats did City suffer in 2002–03?
a)    6
b)    8
c)    9

872.  Who was City's leading goalscorer in City's 2002–03 promotion season with 17 strikes?

873.  How many season tickets did City sell for their return to the FA Premier League in 2003?

a)    10,000
b)    20,000
c)    25,000

874.    Can you name the well-travelled Leicester-born striker who was red-carded on his City debut, in the opening game of the 2004–05 season?

875.    Which former England international defender, now a manager, made his City debut in 2008?

876.    Name the Hearts boss who took over the reins at City after Micky Adams' departure.

877.    What was unusual about City's starting line-up for the third game of the 2005–06 campaign?
a)    there was no player eligible to play for England
b)    it compromised all players signed from Midlands' clubs
c)    all players had represented their country at full international level

878.    Who was unveiled as City's new owner on 13th February 2007?

879.    Who was appointed City's manager, until the end of the 2006-7 season, after the contracts of Kelly and Stowell had been terminated?

880.    Which City manager joked at his press conference when taking the reins at Leicester about signing a long-term contract of 'around six weeks' which proved to be accurate?

881.    At which ground were City relegated to the third tier of English football for the first time in the club's history after drawing 0–0 in the final game of the 2007–08 season?

882.    City finished the 2008–09 season as Champions of League One, setting a string of club records along the way. How many consecutive games did City remain unbeaten?

a)    19
b)    21
c)    23

883.    Matt Fryatt finished the 2008–09 season as City's leading marksmen. How many League goals did he score?

884.    Why was the Championship game against Birmingham City in January 2007 postponed?
a)    freak high winds lifted the roof off the hotel next to the Walkers Stadium depositing it on the concourse next to the ground
b)    the pavements outside the ground were icy
c)    there was an electrical failure after workers cut through a mains cable on Filbert Way

885.    City played Managerial Merry-Go-Round in the first decade of the twenty first century. For the next question all you have to do is determine whether the following managers were in charge of the City for more or less games than their predecessor. In other words are they HIGHER or LOWER; starting with Peter Taylor who managed City for 54 games.

Was
a)    Garry Parker HIGHER or LOWER than Peter Taylor?
b)    Dave Bassett HIGHER or LOWER than Garry Parker?
c)    Micky Adams HIGHER or LOWER than Dave Bassett?
d)    Dave Bassett/Howard Wilkinson HIGHER or LOWER than Micky Adams
e)    Craig Levein HIGHER or LOWER than Dave Bassett/Howard Wilkinson
f)    Rob Kelly HIGHER or LOWER than Craig Levein
g)    Nigel Worthington HIGHER or LOWER than Rob Kelly
h)    Martin Allen HIGHER or LOWER than Nigel Worthington
i)    Jon Rudkin HIGHER or LOWER than Martin Allen
j)    Gary Megson HIGHER or LOWER than Jon Rudkin
k)    Frank Burrows HIGHER or LOWER than Gary Megson
l)    Ian Holloway HIGHER or LOWER than Frank Burrows

# FA Cup Winning Foxes

Although City have never won the FA Cup, several former Foxes have gained winners' medals either before or after signing for Leicester. Can you identify the clubs the following City players won FA Cup winners' medals with?

886.   Paul Cooper
887.   Martin Keown
888.   Emile Heskey
889.   Don Revie
890.   Frank Sinclair
891.   Gary McAllister
892.   Allan Clarke
893.   Kevin Campbell
894.   Laurie Cunningham
895.   Gary Lineker

# International Foxes

City players have won caps with nearly 20 different countries at international level. Can you match the players to the countries they represented?

| | | | |
|---|---|---|---|
| 896. | Theodoros Zagorakis | i) | Wales |
| 897. | Pontus Kåmark | ii) | Turkey |
| 898. | Robbie Savage | iii) | Australia |
| 899. | Matt Elliott | iv) | Hungary |
| 900. | Patrick Kisnorbo | v) | Scotland |
| 901. | Joey Guðjónsson | vi) | Greece |
| 902. | Marton Fülüp | vii) | England |
| 903. | Iain Hume | viii) | Iceland |
| 904. | Ernie Hine | ix) | Sweden |
| 905. | Muzzy Izzet | x) | Canada |

# Record Breakers

Who holds the following club records?

906.   Most Football League appearances for City (528)?

907.   Most first class City appearances (599)?

908.   All-time record goalscorer for City (273)?

909.   Scorer of the highest number of goals for City in a single season (44)?

910.   Scorer of the fastest goal in the club's history (19 seconds)?

911.   Most expensive player purchased by City (c.£5 million)?

912.   Player who attracted the highest transfer fee upon leaving City (£11 million)?

913.   City's oldest debutant (38 years 354 days)?

914.   City's youngest debutant (15 years 203 days)?

915.   City's longest serving manager (10 years)?

916.   Most capped England player whilst on City's books (37)?

917.   Scorer of the most hat-tricks for City (17)?

918.   Scorer of the most penalties for City (41)?

919.   Scorer of the most goals for England whilst playing for City (4)?

920.   Most appearances for City as a substitute (54)?

921.   Scorer of the fastest hat-trick for City (5 minutes)?

922. Scorer of the most goals against City (18)?

923. Leicester's best goalkeeper, in terms of average goals per game conceded (1.18)?

924. Most consecutive appearances for the club (331)?

925. Scorer of the most City goals in the FA Premier League (33)?

# Club Firsts

Can you name City's first...

926.   player to score a 'hat-trick of hat-tricks' against the same opponents

927.   substitute goalkeeper

928.   League opposition at the Walkers Stadium

929.   player to score 6 goals in a single Football League game

930.   player to score a penalty in the FA Premier League

931.   player to be nominated for the European Footballer of the Year award

932.   goalkeeper to score in a Football League game

933.   £1 million player

934.   player to score in the FA Premier League

935.   player to score at the Walkers Stadium in a League game

936.   40 goal a season striker

937.   captain to lift the League Cup

938.   player to score an own goal in the FA Premier League

939.   player to leave the club for more than £1 million

940.   Swedish international player

941.   manager to win the League One Championship

942.  goalkeeper to play for England

943.  player to score a hat-trick against Nottingham Forest

944.  signing to have won the European Cup

945.  shirt sponsors

946.  major trophy

947.  opponents in a European Cup competition

948.  substitute to score for Leicester

949.  £50,000+ signing

# Numbers Game

The answers to the following questions are the numbers below. All you have to do is match the number to the question...

6   7   9   14   16   23   37   78   31,359   31,500   47,298

950.   record Filbert Street attendance

951.   most City home wins in a season

952.   highest number of consecutive wins by City in the Football League

953.   full England international caps won by Gordon Banks as City's goalie

954.   highest number of consecutive unbeaten games by City in the FA Cup

955.   most goals scored by a City player in a single game

956.   fee paid by City in 1971 for the freehold of the Filbert Street ground

957.   longest unbeaten run of League games by City

958.   City's highest average home attendance for a season

959.   total number of City goals scored by Frank Worthington

960. -most away wins by City in a season

# We Hate FOREST

Nottingham Forest are Leicester's arch-rivals. For Leicester's Blue Army it is the first fixture they look out for at the start of each season. How much do you know about City v Forest games?

961.    In what year did City play Forest for the first time in the Football League?

a)      1896
b)      1901
c)      1906

962.    Up until 2011–12 season how many times had City played Forest in the FA Cup?

a)      0
b)      1
c)      4

963.    Forest's record League win was against Leicester Fosse. What was the final score?

a)      Nottingham Forest 6–0 Leicester Fosse
b)      Nottingham Forest 9–0 Leicester Fosse
c)      Nottingham Forest 12–0 Leicester Fosse

964.    What is the highest numbers of goals City have scored against Forest in a single game?

a)      4
b)      5
c)      6

965.    City have never beaten Forest in the League Cup. True or False?

966.    Can you name the former City manager who left Filbert Street to become Forest's manager in the late 1960s?

967. -Which striker left Forest for a then British record transfer fee of £8.5 million in 1995, and a decade later joined Bradford City from City on a free transfer?

968. Which Leicester born player appeared in Forest's European Cup winning side of 1979?

969. On 18 September 2007 Nottingham Forest were given a 'free goal' by Leicester City in a League Cup tie at the City Ground. Why?

970. Who scored a hat-trick for City against Forest in 2012?

# Sven Sven Sven

The arrival of football royalty in the form of the legendary Swedish manager Sven-Göran Eriksson to many Leicester fans meant the start of a new era of success and fame. Nothing however, for Leicester or its Blue Army of fans could possibly be that straightforward...

971.   Prior to joining City how many major trophies did Sven-Göran Eriksson win as a manager?

972.   Which club did Sven-Göran Eriksson manage to two Portuguese Championships, the Portuguese Cup and finishing runners-up in the UEFA Cup?

973.   Can you name two Italian clubs that have been managed by Sven-Göran Eriksson ?

974.   Sven-Göran Eriksson was appointed England manager after the resignation of which famous number seven?

975.   What was the highest FIFA ranking achieved during Sven-Göran Eriksson's reign as England's manager?

976.   Under Sven-Göran Eriksson with England, Darius Vassell scored how many goals from 22 international caps awarded between 2002 and 2004?

977.   Sven-Göran Eriksson was rated by the FA as England's third most successful manager after Alf Ramsey and Bobby Robson. True or False?

978.   Sven-Göran Eriksson became the first manager to win League and Cup doubles in three different countries. True or False?

979.   On 22 July 2009 Sven-Göran Eriksson was appointed as Director of Football at which English League Two club?

980.   Which City chairman appointed Sven-Göran Eriksson as City's manager?

981.   During Sven-Göran Eriksson's reign the name of the Walkers Stadium was changed to reflect the club's new owners. What name was chosen for City's home?

982.    Sven-Göran Eriksson's first League game in charge of City resulted in a 1–1 draw against Hull City, managed by which former Foxes boss?

983.   Can you name centre-half who Sven-Göran Eriksson signed from Reading for £5 million in 2011?

984.   Name the Nigerian striker signed on loan by Sven-Göran Eriksson in 2011, who scored 11 goals for City in 20 appearances.

985.   From which club did Sven-Göran Eriksson sign full-back Lee Peltier in 2011?

986.   Which 'keeper did Sven-Göran Eriksson sign from Leeds United in 2011?

987.   Souleymane 'Sol' Bamba was managed at international level by Sven-Göran Eriksson. What is Sol's nationality?

988.   From which Scottish club did Sven-Göran Eriksson sign Sol Bamba for City?

989.   Sven-Göran Eriksson left Leicester by mutual consent on 24 October 2011 with the Foxes sitting in what position in the Championship?

990.   Who succeeded Sven-Göran Eriksson as City's manager in November 2011?

# And Finally...

991.    Real Madrid beat City 2-1 at the King Power Stadium in July 2011 to win the npower Challenge Cup. Who scored City's goal?

992.    Two players were red-carded twice in 2011-12. Matt Mills was one; can you name the other player?

993.    Who was stripped of City's captaincy in February 2012?

994.    City were knocked out of the League Cup 7-6 on penalties after drawing 2-2 with which club after extra time in round three?

995.    Name the City midfielder whose father was in an act that reached the qualifying stages of the Eurovision Song Contest.

996.    Leicester did the League 'double' over 4 clubs in 2011-12. How many can you name?

997.    Name the 22 year old midfielder signed by City for a fee estimated to be £1 million in January 2012.

998.    Who was City's leading goalscorer in 2011-12?

999.    City's lowest home attendance (16,210) in 2011-12 was for a FA Cup tie against which local rivals?

1,000.  Who won Leicester City's Player of the Year Award for 2011–12?

# Answers

## In the Beginning – Answers

1.    b) 1884
2.    a) Older – Nottingham Forest founded in 1865
      b) Older – Coventry City founded as Singers FC in 1883
      c) Derby County – neither older nor younger founded in the same year as the Fosse, 1884
      d) Older – Birmingham City founded as Small Heath in 1875
      e) Lincoln City – neither older nor younger founded in the same year as the Fosse, 1884
      f) Younger – Peterborough United founded 50 years after the Fosse in 1934
      g) Younger – Northampton Town founded in 1897
3.    Wyggeston School
4.    a) 17 years old
5.    b) ditch
6.    a) iii) private field off Fosse Road
      b) iii) black with diagonal blue sash
      c) i) 1–3–6
      d) i) 5–0
      e) i) Cross bar: YES. The crossbar had been introduced in 1875
          ii) Goal Net: NO. They were not introduced until 1890
          iii) Corner Flags: YES. They were invented in 1872
          iv) Managers Dugout: NO. Aberdeen was the first British club to build a dugout, in the 1920s
          v) White Football: NO. White footballs did not appear in Football League matches until 1951
7.    a) FAIR. Charging a goalkeeper, even when he didn't have the ball was allowed until 1890
      b) FOUL. The two-hands rule was introduced in 1882 because players could hurl the ball miles with one hand

c) FAIR. Until 1912 a goalkeeper could catch the ball anywhere in his own half

d) FAIR. Instead of giving a free kick when a player put the ball behind their goal, corner kicks were introduced in 1872

e) FOUL. Penalties weren't introduced until the start of the 1891–92 season. For the first season it could be a penalty 'dribble'

f) FAIR. The 10 yard rule was not introduced until 1913

g) FOUL. Heading the ball was banned until 1893

8. c) 1s 10d
9. the 'Ancients' or the 'Fossils'
10. c) the Coalville players were unhappy at a decision made by the umpire and walked off the pitch in protest
11. b) spectators were charged a fee to watch the Fosse play for the first time
12. a) Belgrave Road Sports Ground
13. b) outbid by the Leicester Tigers who remained at the ground until 1892 when they moved to the Welford Road site that they still occupy
14. a) the tie was replayed, the Fosse winning 5–0
15. a) Shepshed Albion
16. a) Leicestershire Senior Cup
17. Leicester Fosse Rovers
18. a) 2s 6d a week plus expenses
19. a) Charlie Walker was standing by his goal post unaware that the game had finished
20. to Loughborough to watch a friendly between the Luffs and the Fosse

# Midland League Fosse – Answers

21. a) iii) white shirts and blue breeches
    b) iii) Aylestone Road County Cricket Ground
    c) ii) Derby Junction

d) iii) 4.50pm

e) ii) he became Fosse's manager in 1897 and was suspended indefinitely after being found guilty of poaching players and financial irregularities the following year

f) Fosse 1–0 Derby Junction

g) i) 2 points

22. a) Burton Wanderers 6–0 Fosse

23. Rotherham Town

24. c) 11th- one from the bottom of the Midland League

25. b) Notts Olympic

26. b) runners-up in 1893–94

27. b) Rotherham Town in April 1892

28. a) Leicester Fosse 7–1 Newark

29. False. They were invited to join the Football League in 1894 after Bootle resigned, but the Committee graciously declined the elevation stating that they were 'bound by honour to the Midland League'

30. c) £250 from Aston Villa for Billy Dorrell

## FA Cup Fosse – Answers

31. a) iii) Burton Wanderers

b) i) Mill Lane

c) iii) white shirts and dark blue trousers

d) ii) Leicester Fosse 0–4 Burton Wanderers

e) ii) £15

32. Birmingham City

33. Notts County

34. c) the Loughborough Town captain had his broken leg set by a doctor while still on the pitch

35. c) assaulting a spectator

36. c) Fosse scored 13 goals; Miller and McArthur scored four goals each with a hat-trick from Skea

37. False: Kettering knocked the Fosse out of the Cup three times, but not in consecutive years

38.     1897–98
39.     b)  Southampton
40.     Hinckley Town
41.     a)  Fosse beat Irthlingborough 1–0 away from home in the third
            qualifying round, but were knocked out by Wellingborough
            4–1 in the following fourth qualifying round
42.     a)  torrential downpour flooded the pitch
43.     Market Harborough Town
44.     b)  he was just 4ft 9in tall
45.     b)  it was Leicester's last defeat by non-League opposition until
            Harlow Town in 1980

# Football League Fosse – Answers

46.     a)  i)   Grimsby Town
        b)  David Skea
        c)  i)   pulling up his socks
        d)  ii)  Bailey became the first Fosse player to score an own-goal
                 in the Football League
        e)  i)   Grimsby Town 4–3 Leicester Fosse
        f)  iii) 5,000
47.     J. Lee
48.     c)  Rotherham Town
49.     David Skea
50.     b)  6d
51.     7; the final score was Fosse 9–1 Walsall Town Swifts
52.     c)  Essex County Cricket Club
53.     b)  financial hardship experienced by many supporters in a lock-
            out in the local boot and shoe industry
54.     a)  6,000
55.     One, David Skea was the first Fosse player to score 20 goals in
        a season. Fred Shinton was the only other fosse player to score
        more than 20 goals in a season when he netted a remarkable
        32 times in 1909–10.

56.  b)  fourth
57.  a)  Trent Bridge – Notts County
     b)  Essex County Cricket Ground – Woolwich Arsenal
     c)  Bramall Lane – Sheffield United
58.  Penalty
59.  b)  the goal posts were blown by a gale
60.  Loughborough Town
61.  a)  Fosse beat Division Two champions 2–0 to win the Burford
         Charity Cup and beat Rushden 4–0 in the Rushden Charity
         Cup Final
62.  b)  1897, the limited Company inherited a debt of £1,086 from
         the old Leicester Fosse Committee
63.  b)  haranguing the linesman
64.  Manchester United
65.  a)  Luton Town
66.  c)  Nottingham Forest
67.  a)  12,000
68.  b)  1899
69.  a)  crowd disturbances
70.  c)  Fosse's first home defeat in 39 Football League games
71.  b)  Fosse 7–1 Kaffirs (South Africa)
72.  January 1899
73.  £4
74.  Period of national mourning following the death of Queen
     Victoria
75.  a)  dark blue shirts with light blue collars and sleeves
76.  b)  The Fosse Chronicle
77.  a)  the shot hit a stray dog on the goal-line and rebounded clear.
78.  c)  because they finished bottom of Division Two. Only one
         vote went against the Fosse who topped the re-election poll
         with 33 votes; Stockport County, who finished two places
         above the Fosse were 'relegated' after gaining just 11
         votes.
79.  a)  shorts that were below the knees
80.  a)  7

81.   b)  £395
82.   c)  Leeds City
83.   c)  the same colour as the outfield players
84.   Leicester Fosse beat Stoke City 1–0 away from home to clinch promotion to Division One for the first time in the club's history.
85.   a)  Sheffield Wednesday
86.   Forest beat Fosse 12–0 – the worst defeat in the club's history
87.   No – this was not allowed until 1924
88.   c)  20th – bottom of the League
89.   a)  game was played under electric arc lamps
90.   False
91.   Fred Shinton
92.   a)  he died of peritonitis in Leicester Infirmary within two weeks of his transfer
93.   a)  for playing football on a Sunday
94.   Titanic disaster fund
95.   a)  Sweden
96.   b)  he played for Fosse reserves in the morning and the first team in the afternoon
97.   Only three members of the Fosse side which played in the opening fixtures of the 1913–14 season had cost a fee, £105 in total – Sparrow £90, Mills £5 and Tom Waterall £10.
98.   a)  blue dye was difficult to obtain
99.   c)  72 players
100.  a)  They had to borrow a strip from a local club after losing their kit on the journey to Blundell Park.
101.  b)  As he was preparing to take a goal kick a dog ran from the crowd behind him and unwittingly landed a kick on the dog instead of the ball.
102.  b)  The train carrying Fosse players arrived so late that game had to end when darkness fell.
103.  The Fosse lost the home game 2–4
104.  Fred Shinton – 55 Football League, 3 FA Cup goals
105.  Just one season – 1908–09
106.  c)  8

107.    b)  20th (bottom) of Division One
108.    a)  79 goals
109.    c)  W.A. Henry left the Fosse in November 1911 for £1,000 to join Manchester City.
110.    Twice – 1904 and 1915
111.    True. The Fosse and the 'Luffs' played each other nine times in the Football League, the Fosse P10, W9, D1, L0, F31, A4.
112.    b)  £3,150 3s 3d to be precise

## Nicknames – Answers

113.    a)  True
        b)  False
        c)  False
        d)  False
        e)  True
        f)  False
        g)  True
114.    a)  Sheffield Wednesday
        b)  Grimsby Town;
        c)  Bury FC
        d)  Sheffield United
        e)  Bradford City
        f)  Preston North End
        g)  Bristol City
        h)  Everton.
115.    a)  Denis Rofe
        b)  Graham Cross
        c)  Arthur Chandler
        d)  Allan Clarke
        e)  Emile Heskey
        f)  Paul Dichov
        g)  George Armstrong
        h)  Derek Dougan.

# A Year You Remember? – Answers

116. c) 1994
117. a) 1928
118. b) 1974
119. a) 2003
120. b) 1969
121. c) 1957
122. a) 1964
123. b) 2000
124. a) 1993
125. c) 1966

# High Flying City 1919–30 – Answers

126. Peter Hodge
127. Wolverhampton Wanderers
128. a) Fulham
129. c) he scored a hat-trick and was sent off for fighting
130. King George V
131. Jock Paterson in City's 4–0 victory over Lincoln City in a Football League Division Two game in March 1920.
132. Jock Paterson
133. Stockport County
134. Raith Rovers
135. Queen's Park Rangers
136. Arthur Chandler
137. b) an inferior goal average
138. Johnny Duncan
139. b) 62
140. b) 100

141. b) it was scored direct from a corner-kick – only the second time this feat had been achieved since the rule change allowed for the possibility

142. Football League Division Two Championship

143. Manchester City

144. Johnny Duncan

145. Willie Orr

146. a) The Knuts

147. Leicester went to the top of Division One for the first time in their history

148. Portsmouth

149. six swans flew over Filbert Street

150. a) 18–0

151. So as not to alert defenders of his weaker knee

152. Ernie Hine

153. Sheffield Wednesday

154. a) for financial reasons

# Hat-trick Heroes – Answers

155. Keith Weller

156. Ken Keyworth

157. Frank Worthington

158. Gary Lineker

159. Stan Collymore

160. Matt Fryatt

161. Matt Fryatt

162. Paul Gallagher

163. Steve Howard

164. David Connolly

165. Jeffrey Schlupp

# Yo-Yo Years 1930–39 – Answers

166.   George Ritchie
167.   David Halliday
168.   b)  the net
169.   b)  health grounds
170.   Ernie Hine
171.   b)  train carriage was involved in a shunting incident
172.   Willie Orr
173.   a)  torrential downpour caused the fans to run for cover
174.   Stanley Matthews
175.   Sandy McLaren
176.   b)  stray ball after the whistle has been blown
177.   a)  Portsmouth
       b)  St Andrews, Birmingham
       c)  Leicester City 1–4 Portsmouth
       d)  Sep Smith
178.   Peter Hodge
179.   Arthur Lochhead
180.   a)  two referees officiated and two linesmen officiated the game in a FA experiment.
181.   Ernie Hine
182.   Football League had a dispute with the Football Pools companies over the copyright of the fixture list. In an escalation of the dispute the Football League tore up the fixture list in the 1935–36 season and delayed the announcement of each of the following Saturday's fixtures until the day before.
183.   False. The suggestion was made but the idea was turned down by the Board
184.   John (Jack) Bowers
185.   Frank Womack
186.   Wolverhampton Wanderers
187.   Shirt numbers

188.   Malwyn (Mal) Griffiths
189.   Frank Womack
190.   a) Three (W2, L1). World War Two started in September 1939 and football was stopped.

# Foul Football – Answers

191.   a) poaching a player
192.   b) indiscipline and insubordination, thought to have been alcohol-related
193.   b) allocation of pegs in the changing room
194.   a) the Football League rules at the time stated that players shorts should be below the knees
195.   c) leaving the field to seek shelter from the rain
196.   Johnny Duncan
197.   Irregularities found in the club's pre-war financial record (payment of excessive bonuses, signing-on fees etc)
198.   Ken Chisholm
199.   he suggested that the referee should get some spectacles
200.   Gordon Banks
201.   Don Revie
202.   Keith Weller
203.   Because the Derby v Fulham game at the Baseball Ground was abandoned 75 seconds before the 90 minutes were up. Fulham, who were trailing 1–0 at the time, could have pipped City for third place with a victory.
204.   Dennis Wise
205.   Alex 'Hurricane' Higgins
206.   Garry Parker
207.   Frank Sinclair
208.   Baring his bottom to the crowd
209.   their ticket distribution for the 1999 Worthington Cup Final

210. Stan Collymore
211. Robbie Savage
212. Paul Dickov, Keith Gillespie and Frank Sinclair
213. Dennis Wise
214. first Leicester player to be sent-off in a Football League match at Filbert Street
215. b) 8
216. Steve Walsh
217. Len Chalmers
218. Kevin MacDonald
219. Alan Young
220. Ian Wilson
221. for breaking the jaw of the Shrewsbury striker David Geddis on the opening day of the season
222. Paul Ramsey
223. David Speedie
224. Garry Parker
225. Peter Shilton
226. Carl Muggleton
227. David Speedie
228. b) 8
229. 3
230. Matt Elliott
231. Justin Edinburgh
232. Clint Hill
233. Patrick Kisnorbo
234. Jack Hobbs
235. Alan Smith
236. Dion Dublin
237. Martyn Waghorn, Richie Wellens, Steve Howard

238. Miguel Vitor
239. Kevin Pressman
240. Darius Vassell

# Wartime and the 1940s City – Answers

241. Johnny Duncan
242. Tom Bromilow
243. Arsenal
244. c) goal average
245. b) Football League Midlands Division
246. Tommy Lawton
247. True
248. George Dewis
249. Tom Maher
250. b) all ties up to and including the sixth round were played on a two-legged basis
251. Johnny Duncan
252. Mal Griffiths
253. Watford
254. True
255. Highbury (Arsenal)
256. Don Revie
257. Norman Plummer
258. Septimus Smith
259. Norman Bullock
260. b) 30,384
261. c) 21 shilling
262. a) 35
263. Johnny Duncan (City), Stan Cullis (Wolverhampton Wanderers)
264. Norman Plummer (City), Billy Wright (Wolves)
265. Blue
266. Don Revie

267.    Walter Harrison

268.    Gordon Bradley

269.    Leicester City 0–2 Wolverhampton Wanderers

270.    Mal Griffths

271.    Ken Chisholm

272.    Jesse Pye

273.    Jimmy Harrison

274.    City 1–3 Wolverhampton Wanderers

275.    Princess Elizabeth (later to become Queen Elizabeth II)

# Club Connections – Answers

276.    Southampton

277.    Gillingham

278.    Liverpool

279.    Luton Town

280.    Coventry City

281.    Queen's Park Rangers

282.    Chelsea

283.    Notts County

284.    Leeds United

285.    West Bromwich Albion

286.    Crystal Palace

287.    Norwich City

288.    Glasgow Celtic

289.    Charlton Athletic

290.    Bradford City

291.    Aston Villa

292.    Everton

293.    Derby County

294.    Brighton & Hove Albion

295.    Ipswich Town

## 1950s City – Answers

296.    a)  18th Division One 1957–58 season
297.    Three – Norman Bullock, David Halliday and Matt Gillies
298.    True
299.    a)  Franklin was unwilling to move
300.    Matt Gillies
301.    a)  Festival of Britain
302     a)  £14
303.    c)  85
304.    b)  oxygen
305.    b)  Everton
306.    Matt Gillies
307.    Norman Bullock
308.    c)  31,359
309.    Lincoln City
310.    David Halliday
311.    Willie Gardiner
312.    scored the only official joint own-goal
313.    John Doherty
314.    c)  112
315.    b)  Borussia Dortmund
316.    b)  Leicester City 8 – Manchester City 4
317.    Chesterfield
318.    Birmingham City
319.    Jimmy Walsh
320.    Manchester United

## The Gunner – Answers

321.    Fulham
322.    he was signed as a cheap replacement to the well-liked City
        striker Jack Lee
323.    10
324.    0

325.   7
326.   b)  Don Revie
327.   Arthur Chandler
328.   b)  44
329.   c)  434
330.   b)  122
331.   David Halliday
332.   b)  16
333.   Willie Gardiner
334.   Shrewsbury Town
335.   True

# Pools Panel – Answers

336.   a)  10–0
337.   c)  3–1
338.   b)  1–1
339.   a)  6–6
340.   c)  12–0
341.   b)  7–1
342.   c)  5–2
343.   b)  1–1
344.   b)  1–2
345.   b)  0–2
346.   a)  1–1
347.   c)  5–0
348.   c)  3–2
349.   a)  0–0
350.   c)  2–1
351.   b)  0–4
352.   b)  0–5
353.   c)  1–2
354.   a)  1–0
355.   c)  2–0

## Retired but Not Forgotten – Answers

356.  Peter Rodrigues
357.  Dion Dublin
358.  Jamie Lawrence
359.  Muzzy Izzet
360.  Mark Wallington
361.  Alan Young
362.  Roger Davies
363.  Derek Dougan
364.  Keith Weller
365.  Len Glover
366.  Steve Walsh
367.  Laurie Cunningham
368.  Garry Parker
369.  Alan Woollett
370.  Graham Cross

## Swinging 60s City – Answers

371.  None
372.  a) 4th Division One in 1962–63
373.  Jock Wallace
374.  b) City's first all-ticket home game
375.  Ritchie Norman
376.  a) Stamford Bridge
377.  Jimmy Walsh
378.  Tottenham Hotspur
379.  b) quagmire
380.  Oxford United
381.  Elland Road (Leeds), City Ground (Nottingham), St Andrew's (Birmingham)
382.  Colin Appleton

383. Howard Riley
384. Les Allen
385. Bill Nicholson
386. Danny Blanchflower
387. Ken Leek
388. Hugh McIlmoyle
389. He had been on England duty at Wembley
390. He was still serving his National Service
391. York City
392. The winter of 1963 was the severest for many decades. City had a record-breaking run of 16 games undefeated, including 10 successive wins.
393. chemically treated topsoil which generated enough heat to melt the ice
394. Denis Law and Ken Keyworth
395. Liverpool and Mike Stringfellow
396. Leicester City
397. White with a blue trim around the collar and cuffs
398. a) John Sjoberg
     b) Mike Stringfellow
399. Howard Riley and Graham Cross
400. Colin Appleton and Noel Cantwell
401. To avoid a 'colour clash' for black and white TV viewers
402. Leicester City 0–1 Manchester United
403. Ken Keyworth
404. David Herd (2), Denis Law
405. b) Double Decker was reroofed and the Enclosure re-terraced
406. True
407. Malcolm Musgrove
408. 1960
409. West Ham United
410. Two legged semi-final, first leg at Filbert Street, second leg at Upton Park
411. 1–1
412. Dave Gibson

413.  Colin Appleton
414.  Coventry City
415.  Plymouth Argyle
416.  b)  Tommy Docherty
417.  c)  Chelsea 3–2 City
418.  Terry Venables
419.  Colin Appleton
420.  b)  Chelsea 3–2 City
421.  Derek Dougan
422.  1 own-goal and two for City
423.  John Sjoberg
424.  Frank McLintock
425.  Bobby Roberts
426.  Ken Keyworth (1961–62; 1962–63; 1963–64)
427.  Peter Shilton
428.  Stoke City
429.  Len Glover
430.  1968
431.  Nottingham Forest
432.  Torquay United
433.  b)  21st Division One
434.  Manchester United
435.  O'Farrell's policy of naming a 14-man squad on the Friday before a match, rather than the starting line-up

## Managers as Players – Answers

436.  Micky Adams
437.  Craig Levein
438.  Frank O'Farrell
439.  Brian Little
440.  Sven-Göran Eriksson
441.  Martin Allen

442.  Paulo Sousa

443.  Mark McGhee

444.  Arthur Lochhead

445.  Bryan Hamilton

446.  Peter Taylor

447.  Nigel Worthington

448.  Gary Megson

449.  Frank McLintock

450.  Martin O'Neill

## 1969 FA Cup Final – Answers

451.  a) 5 (Barnsley, Millwall, Liverpool, Mansfield Town and West Bromwich Albion)

452.  False, they beat Mansfield Town 1–0 away from home

453.  a) cabbage patch

454.  Manchester City

455.  a) 16,000

456.  a) to play on any nerves Leicester players may have had

457.  Peter Rodrigues (Welsh); David Gibson and Andy Lochhead (Scottish)

458.  b) touch line ban

459.  a) Princess Anne

460.  Peter Shilton, Graham Cross and Alan Woollett

461.  Tony Book

462.  Red and black striped shirt, black shorts and socks

463.  Manchester City 1–0 Leicester City

464.  Neil Young

465.  John Sjoberg

466.  Len Glover

467.   Andy Lochhead
468.   Allan Clarke
469.   False. They won the Cup Winners' Cup beating Górnik Zabrze 2–1 in the Final.
470.   True

## Transfer Trail – Answers

471.   Steve Claridge
472.   Allan Clarke
473.   Muzzy Izzet
474.   David Nish
475.   Russell Osman
476.   Don Revie
477.   Arthur Rowley
478.   Jon Samuels
479.   Ian Walker
480.   Matt Fryatt

## City in the Play-offs – Answers

481.   1987
482.   Four – 1992, 1993, 1994 and 1996
483.   Ian Ormondroyd
484.   a) 4th
       b) John Beck
       c) ii) 5
       d) Kevin 'Rooster' Russell
       e) 6–1
485.   a) Steve Walsh
       b) Kenny Dalglish

    c) David Speedie
    d) Mike Newell
    e) Carl Muggleton

486.  a) ii) Crystal Palace
    b) demolition of the Main Stand at Filbert Street to make way for the Carling Stand
    c) Guy Whittingham
    d) Julian Joachim
    e) 2–2

487.  a) Gary Mills
    b) Glenn Hoddle
    c) Steve Thompson
    d) Paul Bodin

488.  a) Gavin Ward
    b) David Speedie
    c) Steve Walsh
    d) Simon Grayson
    e) Jimmy Willis

489.  a) Stoke City
    b) Garry Parker
    c) Kevin Poole
    d) Steve Walsh
    e) Garry Parker
    f) Andy Roberts
    g) Zelijko Kalac
    h) Steve Claridge
    i) Nigel Martyn

490.  a) Newcastle United
    b) Bluebirds
    c) five times – twice in the League, once in the FA Cup and twice in the Play-offs
    d) True
    e) 0–1
    f) 3–3
    g) Yann Kermorgant
    h) D.J. Campbell

# O'Neill's Arrivals Board – Answers

a)   Neil Lennon – Crewe Alexandra
b)   Spencer Prior – Norwich City
c)   Kasey Keller – Millwall
d)   Gerry Taggart – Bolton Wanderers
e)   Matt Elliott – Oxford United
f)   Tony Cottee – Selangor
g)   Ian Marshall – Ipswich Town
h)   Pegguy Arphexad – Lens
i)   Steve Claridge – Birmingham City
j)   Robbie Savage – Crewe Alexandra
k)   Muzzy Izzet – Chelsea
l)   Steve Guppy – Port Vale
m)   Theodoros Zagorakis – PAOK
n)   Tim Flowers – Blackburn Rovers
o)   Andrew Impey – West Ham United

# The 70s – the Bloomfield era & Glam Football – Answers

491.   b)  7th Division One (1975–76)
482.   b)  1 (1977–78)
493.   True
494.   David Nish
495.   City won 1–0, but not before Villa's McMahon's shot had clearly entered the net, hit the rear stanchion and rebounded into play. The referee waved play on and an incensed Villa were doomed to Division Three.
496.   Don Revie
497.   Ally Brown
498.   Frank McLintock
499.   Eddie Kelly

500. David Nish
501. Ally Brown (15 goals)
502. John Sjoberg
503. Manchester United
504. Liverpool
505. Arsenal
506. Leyton Orient
507. Jon Samuels
508. David Nish
509. Frank Worthington
510. Frank Worthington
511. Frank Worthington
512. Gordon Banks
513. Alex Stepney
514. Dennis Rofe
515. Steve Earle
516. Stoke City
517. Liverpool
518. John Toshack
519. Because he refused to take the field in December 1974 for the second half against Ipswich Town having had a transfer request turned down.
520. Brian Kidd
521. 1 (1973-4)
522. Graham Cross
523. David Nish
524. Alan Birchenall
525. c) 34,000
526. Jeff Blockley
527. Bob Lee
528. Jon Samuels, Keith Weller, Alan Birchenall, Mark Wallington, Frank Worthington, Dennis Rofe
529. Chris Nicoll

530.    Alan Birchenall

531.    1977

532.    a)  11th

533.    b)  22nd

534.    a)  5

535.    a)  Arsenal

       b)  Derby County

       c)  Club Brugge

       d)  Queen's Park Rangers

       e)  Liverpool

       f)  Queen's Park Rangers

536.    Roger Davies and Geoff Salmons

537.    Glasgow Rangers

538.    Running up and down sand hills

539.    Bob Lee

540.    Johann Cruyff

541.    Crystal Palace

542.    John O'Neill

543.    Tom Bloor

544.    Trevor Christie

545.    Oldham Athletic

546.    Sunderland

547.    Bill Henderson

548.    scored in his 4th City game against Notts County in April 1979

549.    Frank Worthington (1972–73; 1973–74; 1974–75; 1976–77)

550.    c)  5th round in 1970–71

# Managers, Gaffers & Bosses – Answers

551.    Not Sacked

552.    Not Sacked

553.    Sacked

554. Sacked
555. Not Sacked
556. Not Sacked
557. Not Sacked
558. Not Sacked
559. Not Sacked
560. Sacked
561. Hull City
562. Manchester City
563. Nottingham Forest
564. Blackpool
565. Coventry City
566. Motherwell
567. Aston Villa
568. Wigan
569. Queen's Park Rangers
570. Wycombe Wanderers
571. Gary Rowett
572. Paul Dickov
573. Simon Grayson
574. Roberto Mancini
575. Chris Powell
576. Micky Adams
577. Martin O'Neill
578. Bryan Hamilton
579. Peter Taylor
580. Craig Levein
581. Sven-Göran Eriksson
582. Don Revie
583. Johnny Duncan
584. Arthur Lochhead
585. Peter Hodge
586. Brian Little

587.  Matt Gillies

588.  Peter Hodge

589.  Brian Little

590.  Paulo Sousa

# 1980s – The Wilderness Years – Answers

591.  b)  15th Division One in both 1983–84 and 1984–85

592.  4 – Jock Wallace, Gordon Milne, Bryan Hamilton, David Pleat

593.  Gary Lineker

594.  Gary Lineker

595.  Kenilworth Road (Luton Town), Boundary Park (Oldham Athletic), Loftus Road (Queen's Park Rangers)

596.  Jim Melrose

597.  Andy Peake

598.  Beat Liverpool at Anfield

599.  Exeter City

600.  Motherwell

601.  Coventry City

602.  There was a hat-trick of penalties (for the only time in City's history); a Lineker hat-trick (including one of the penalties) plus a Steve Lynex hat-trick (2 penalties).

603.  Steve Lynex

604.  Mark Wallington

605.  Alan Smith

606.  Tom English

607.  c)  26

608.  a)  Burnley

b)  0–0

c)  yes

609. Because the Derby v Fulham game at the Baseball Ground was abandoned 75 seconds before the 90 minutes were up. Fulham could have pipped City for third place with a victory who were trailing 1–0 at the time.

610. Alan Birchenall

611. Mark Grew

612. Ind Coope

613. Arthur Chandler

614. a) Vice-president

615. Nottingham Forest

616. b) 5,000th League goal

617. Liverpool

618. Three teeth – they were knocked out when he was fouled, they found them after a search through the grass, they were then fixed back in his mouth in hospital.

619. Aberdeen

620. Gary Lineker

621. Motherwell

622. Steve Whitworth

623. Ian Andrews

624. Derby County

625. Everton

626. Mark Bright

627. Bryan Hamilton

628. Steve Walsh

629. Steve Moran

630. Laurie Cunningham

631. Gary Lineker

632. Alan Smith

633. Jari Rantanen

634. a) 7

635.   Mike Newell
636.   7
637.   Alan Smith
638.   Paul Cooper
639.   Tottenham Hotspur
640.   Peter Weir

## Strike Force – Answers

641.   Ken Keyworth
642.   Mark Robins
643.   D.J. Campbell
644.   Iwan Roberts
645.   Dion Dublin
646.   Tony Cottee
647.   Matt Fryatt
648.   Alan Smith
649.   Darius Vassell
650.   Paul Dickov
651.   Jermaine Beckford
652.   Frank Worthington
653.   Arthur Chandler
654.   Derek Hines
655.   Emile Heskey
656.   Steve Claridge
657.   David Nugent
658.   Paul Gallagher
659.   Steve Howard
660.   Brian Deane

# Name that Gaffer – Answers

661.  Brian Little
662.  Gordon Lee
663.  Martin Allen
664.  Martin O'Neill
665.  Matt Gillies
666.  Frank O'Farrell
667.  Gordon Milne
668.  Frank McLintock
669.  Jock Wallace
670.  Gary Megson
671.  Rob Kelly
672.  Mark McGhee
673.  David Pleat
674.  Micky Adams
675.  Bryan Hamilton
676.  Sven-Göran Eriksson
677.  Paulo Sousa
678.  Craig Levein
679.  Nigel Pearson
680.  Ian Holloway
681.  Dave Bassett
682.  Jimmy Bloomfield
683.  Peter Taylor
684.  Matt Gillies
685.  Nigel Worthington

# Book 'em! – Answers

686.  Stan Collymore
687.  Frank Worthington
688.  Brian Little
689.  Steve Claridge

690.  Alan Birchenall
691.  Peter Shilton
692.  Gary Lineker
693.  Steve Walsh
694.  Frank McLintock
695.  Don Revie

# 1969–89 Sweet FA Cup City – Answers

696.  twice (1974 and 1981)
697.  David Webb
698.  True: 42,000 a capacity at the time for Filbert Street
699.  Arsenal (1970–71, 1972–73, 1974–75)
700.  Keith Weller
701.  Liverpool
702.  Leatherhead negotiated a switch of venue to Filbert Street to make more money
703.  2–0
704.  Chris Kelly – Leatherhead's loud mouthed striker
705.  4
706.  Joe Waters
707.  Alan Young
708.  Keith Weller
709.  Harlow Town
710.  Exeter City
711.  3 (Mark Wallington, Alan Young and Steve Lynex)
712.  Tommy Williams
713.  Falklands War (against Ardiles home country, Argentina) had started just days before the match
714.  Ian Wilson
715.  Burton Albion

# 1990s...the Glory Years – Answers

716.   b)  9th FA Premier League
717.   David Pleat, Gordon Lee, Brian Little, Mark McGhee, Martin O'Neill
718.   six
719.   twice
720.   Leeds United
721.   b)  It was the first live transmission of a City game
722.   Terry Shipman
723.   Steve Walsh
724.   Tony James
725.   Gordon Lee
726.   Darlington
727.   Gary Coatsworth, Jimmy Willis and Michael Trotter
728.   Allan Evans, John Gregory, Steve Hunt
729.   Zenith Data Systems
730.   b)  1992–93
731.   Sheffield Wednesday
732.   Ian Ormondroyd and Phil Gee
733.   b)  Construction of the Carling Stand meant that the ground only had two floodlight pylons
734.   David Kelly
735.   Steve Walsh
736.   Newcastle United
737.   Mark Draper
738.   Julian Joachim
739.   Tottenham Hotspur
740.   b)  Jimmy Willis
741.   c)  personal reasons
742.   Allan Evans

743. Ian Ormondroyd
744. Kevin MacDonald and Tony McAndrew
745. David Lowe
746. Mark McGhee
747. Reading
748. 12 months
749. Mark Robins
750. Manchester City
751. Aston Villa
752. Jamie Lawrence
753. b) 8
754. Emile Heskey
755. Iwan Roberts
756. Neil Lennon
757. b) £3.25 million
758. Brighton & Hove Albion
759. Julian Joachim
760. Wolves
761. Norwich City
762. a) 8th FA Premier League (1999–2000)
763. 4½ years – December 1995–June 2000
764. Pontus Kåmark
765. Steve Corica & Želijko Kalac
766. Garry Parker
767. Manchester City
768. Graham Fenton
769. Garry Parker
770. Leicester City 3–3 Arsenal
771. Ian Marshall
772. Garry Parker
773. 110p
774. Sir Rodney Walker
775. Tony Cottee
776. Mark McGhee

777. English Fair Play League – for the least bookings/dismissals received during the season
778. Steve Guppy
779. Gerry Taggart
780. Frank Sinclair
781. Muzzy Izzet
782. Darren Eadie
783. Tony Cottee
784. three – 1997, 1999, 2000
785. Wimbledon
786. Rob Ullathorne
787. Bryan Robson
788. Juninho Paulister
789. Kasey Keller and Muzzy Izzet
790. Fabrizio Ravanelli
791. 2 minutes
792. Hillsborough
793. Steve Claridge
794. Steve Walsh
795. Tony Cottee
796. Tottenham Hotspur
797. Steve Walsh
798. Tony Cottee and Emile Heskey
799. Leicester City 0–0 Tottenham Hotspur
800. Justin Edinburgh
801. Allan Nielsen
802. John Gregory
803. Tranmere Rovers
804. Martin O'Neill
805. Tim Flowers
806. Matt Elliott
807. Robbie Savage
808. Leicester City 2–1 Tranmere Rovers
809. Matt Elliott
810. Ian Rush

## Jeepers Keepers – Answers

811.  Chris Weale
812.  Kevin Pressman
813.  Gordon Bradley
814.  Tim Flowers
815.  Sandy McLaren
816.  Mark Wallington
817.  Pegguy Arphexad
818.  Gordon Banks
819.  Márton Fülöp
820.  Martin Hodge
821.  Peter Shilton
822.  Kasey Keller
823.  Carl Muggleton
824.  Kevin Poole
825.  éelijko Kalac
826.  Chris Kirkland
827.  Ian Walker
828.  Horace Bailey
829.  Kasper Schmeichel
830.  George Hebden

## Leicester or Not? – Answers

831.  Local
832.  Not Local
833.  Not Local
834.  Not Local
835.  Local
836.  Local
837.  Not Local
838.  Not Local
839.  Local
840.  Local

841. Local
842. Not Local
843. Not Local
844. Not Local
845. Local
846. Not Local
847. Local
848. Not Local
849. Local
850. Local

# Twenty-first century City 2000–10 – Answers

851. b) 8th FA Premier League (1999–2000)
852. 11
853. 3 (2000–01, 2001–02, 2003–04)
854. Peter Taylor, Gillingham
855. Wolverhampton Wanderers
856. 13
857. Tim Flowers
858. b) Top of the Premier League
859. a) Red Star Belgrade
       b) Gerry Taggart
       c) Turbulent political situation in Serbia
       d) 2–4
860. Emile Heskey for Liverpool
861. Les Ferdinand
862. LG Electronics
863. Bolton Wanderers
864. Roberto Mancini
865. 15 months
866. Leicester City 0–6 Leeds United

867. Ade Akinibiyi
868. b) £50 million
869. a) Mark McGhee
    b) Alan Birchenall announced that the club had been saved from bankruptcy by a consortium headed by Lineker
    c) because Millwall had banned City fans at the game held at the New Den a month earlier
    d) Dennis Wise
    e) Steve Claridge
    f) 4–1
870. c) 90 per cent
871. a) 6
872. Paul Dickov
873. b) 20,000
874. Dion Dublin
875. Chris Powell
876. Craig Levein
877. a) no player eligible to play for England
878. Milan Mandaric
879. Nigel Worthington
880. Gary Megson
881. Victoria Ground, Stoke City
882. c) 23
883. 27
884. a) freak high winds lifted the roof off the hotel next to the Walkers Stadium depositing it on the concourse next to the ground
885. a) Lower (1 v 54)
    b) Higher (28 v 1)
    c) Higher (110 v 4)
    d) Lower (4 v 110)
    e) Higher (70 v 4)
    f) Lower (63 v 70)

g) Lower (5 v 63)
h) Lower (4 v 5)
i) Lower (1 v 4)
j) Higher (9 v 1)
k) Lower (5 v 9)
l) Higher (32 v 5)

# FA Cup Winning Foxes – Answers

886. Ipswich Town (1978)
887. Arsenal (1998, 2002 & 2003)
888. Liverpool (2001)
889. Manchester City (1956)
890. Chelsea (1997)
891. Liverpool (2001)
892. Leeds United (1972)
893. Arsenal (1993)
894. Wimbledon (1988)
895. Tottenham Hotspur (1991)

# International Foxes – Answers

896. Theodoros Zagorakis – vi) Greece
897. Pontus Kåmark – ix) Sweden
898. Robbie Savage – i) Wales
899. Matt Elliott – v) Scotland
900. Patrick Kisnorbo – iii) Australia
901. Joey Guðjónsson – viii) Iceland
902. Martin Fülüp – iv) Hungary
903. Iain Hume – x) Canada
904. Ernie Hine – vii) England
905. Muzzy Izzet – ii) Turkey

# Record Breakers – Answers

906. Adam Black
907. Graham Cross
908. Arthur Chandler
909. Arthur Rowley
910. Matt Fryatt
911. Ade Akinbiyi
912. Emile Heskey
913. Chris Powell – 38 years 354 days v Fulham, League Cup, away, 28 August 2008
914 Ashley Chambers – 15 years 203 days as substitute v Blackpool, League Cup second round, 20 September 2005
915. Matt Gillies is Leicester City's longest serving manager (November 1958 to November 1968), but George Johnson (September 1898 to June 1912) is the club's longest serving secretary-manager.
916. Gordon Banks
917. Arthur Chandler
918. Arthur Rowley
919. Ernie Hine
920. Trevor Benjamin
921. Fred Shinton
922. Dixie Dean
923. Peter Shilton
924. Mark Wallington
925. Emile Heskey & Muzzy Izzet

# Club Firsts – Answers

926. Arthur Chandler vs Aston Villa
927. Gavin Ward for Kevin Poole

928.   Watford
929.   Johnny Duncan
930.   Garry Parker
931.   Godron Banks
932.   Peter Shilton
933.   Mark Draper
934.   Julian Joachim (Newcastle United)
935.   Brian Deane
936.   Arthur Rowley
937.   Colin Appleton
938.   Jimmy Willis
939.   Gary McAllister
940.   Pontus Kåmark
941.   Nigel Pearson
942.   Horace Bailey
943.   Don Revie
944.   Gary Mills
945.   Ind Coope
946.   League Cup (1964)
947.   Glenavon (1961)
948.   Tom Sweenie (1966)
949.   Len Glover

# Numbers Game – Answers

950.   47,298 (v Tottenham Hotspur FA Cup fifth round 1928)
951.   16
952.   7 (on 4 occasions)
953.   37
954.   9
955.   6 (Johnny Duncan 1924 and Arthur Chandler in 1928)
956.   31,500

957.   23 (1 November 2008–7 March 2009)
958.   31,359
959.   78
960.   14

## We Hate FOREST – Answers

961.   c)   1906 – City lost 5–1 at the City Ground
962.   b)   1 – in 1901 Forest won 5–1
963.   c)   12–0 (1909)
964.   b)   five in 1913
965.   False – they have played each other twice (1988 and 2007)
       and have each won once
976.   Matt Gillies
987.   Stan Collymore
998.   Peter Shilton
969.   It was a rescheduled match after their original meeting on 28th
       August, which Forest were leading 1–0, was abandoned after
       the Leicester player Clive Clarke collapsed in the dressing room
       at half-time. City won the match 3–2.
970.   Jermaine Beckford

## Sven Sven Sven – Answers

971.   17
972.   Benefica
973.   Roma, Sampdoria, Fiorentina, Lazio
974.   Kevin Keegan
975.   5th
976.   6
977.   False – he was rated second to Ramsey

978.   True
979.   Notts County
980.   Vichal Raksriaksorn
981.   King Power Stadium
982.   Nigel Pearson
983.   Matt Mills
984.   Yakubu Aiyegbeni
985.   Huddersfield Town
986.   Kasper Schmeichel
987.   Ivory Coast
988.   Hibernian
989.   13th position
990.   Nigel Pearson

# And Finally Answers

991.   Lloyd Dyer
992.   Neil Danns
993.   Matt Mills
994.   Cardiff City
995.   Neil Danns
996.   Coventry City, Derby County, Crystal Palace and Southampton
997.   Danny Drinkwater
998.   David Nugent (15 League goals)
999.   Nottingham Forest
1,000.  Kasper Schmeichel